HUMAN BRAIN AND SENSES
RESOURCES

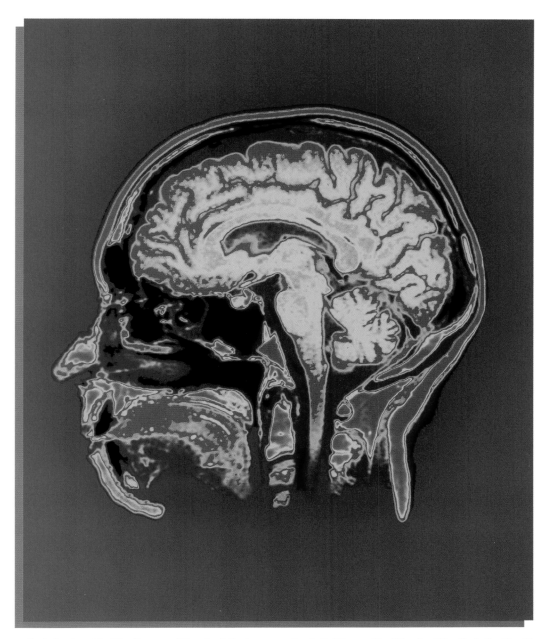

IMAGES, DATA, AND READINGS

DEVELOPED AT LAWRENCE HALL OF SCIENCE, UNIVERSITY OF CALIFORNIA AT BERKELEY
PUBLISHED AND DISTRIBUTED BY DELTA EDUCATION

FOSS Middle School Project Staff and Associates

FOSS Middle School Curriculum Development Team
Dr. Lawrence F. Lowery, Principal Investigator
Linda De Lucchi, Co-Director
Larry Malone, Co-Director
Sue Jagoda, Curriculum Developer
Anthony Cody, Curriculum Developer
Dr. Susan Brady, Curriculum Developer
Dr. Kathy Long, Assessment Coordinator
Cheryl Webb, Program Assistant
Carol Sevilla, Graphic Designer
Rose Craig, Artist
Lisa Baker, Artist
Mark Warren, Equipment Manager

ScienceVIEW Multimedia Design Team
Dr. Marco Molinaro, Director
Dr. Susan Ketchner, Project Manager
Leigh Anne McConnaughey, Principal Illustrator; **Wolf Read,** Senior Illustrator
Sue Whitmore, Senior Illustrator; **Amy Todd,** Illustrator; **Johnny Chen,** Illustrator Assistant
Richard Blair, Head Programmer; **Susan Surapruik,** Programmer
Richard Hyde, System Administrator; **Loretta Hintz,** Video Editor
Igor Spivak, Student Assistant; **Alicia Nieves,** Quality Assurance
Guillaume Brasseur, Computer Administrator and QA Manager

Special Contributors and Consultants
Richard C. Van Sluyters, OD, PhD, Science Consultant; **Stefan Arnold,** MRI Technician; **Marshall Montgomery,** Materials Design
Rockman, ET AL., Evaluators

Delta Education FOSS Middle School Team
Mathew Bacon, Jeanette Wall, Bonnie Piotrowski, Tom Guetling, Dave Vissoe, Grant Gardner, John Prescott
Joann Hoy, editor; **Cathrine Monson,** proofreader

National Trial Teachers
Evelyn Rayford, North Heights Junior High School, Texarkana, AR; **John Rhodes,** Utterback Magnet Middle School, Tucson, AZ
Lorraine Clayton, Southeast Middle School, Fresno, CA; **Robert Sherriff,** Parsons Middle School, Redding, CA
Maria Little, Borel Middle School, San Mateo, CA; **Carol LeCrone,** Mt. Garfield Middle School, Clifton, CO
Kathy Ludlam, Grand Mesa Middle School, Grand Junction, CO; **Sheree Vessels,** Southern Oaks Middle School, Port St. Lucie, FL
Lisa Weber, Springfield Middle School, Holland, OH; **Ken Groch,** Springfield Middle School, Holland, OH
Jean Ross, Derby Middle School, Derby, KS; **Joe Mishley,** Hudson High School, Hudson, MA
Terry Doud, Heritage Middle School, W. St. Paul, MN; **Gayle Dunlap,** Walter T. Bergen Middle School, Bloomingdale, NJ
Donna Moran, Walter T. Bergen Middle School, Bloomingdale, NJ; **Joan Caroselli,** J. E. Soehl Middle School, Linden, NJ
Nicole Kennedy, Sarah Garnett Middle School #324, Brooklyn, NY; **Barbara Cabbil,** Morningside Middle School, Fort Worth, TX
Chris Bryant, Jackson Technology Center, Garland, TX; **Virginia Reid,** Thurgood Marshall Middle School, Olympia, WA
Scott Stier, Badger Middle School, West Bend, WI; **Doug Zarling,** Badger Middle School, West Bend, WI

Lawrence Hall of Science

FOSS for Middle School Project
Lawrence Hall of Science, University of California
Berkeley, CA 94720 510-642-8941

...because children learn by doing.®

Delta Education
P.O. Box 3000 80 Northwest Blvd.
Nashua, NH 03063   1-800-258-1302

The FOSS Middle School Program was developed in part with the support of the National Science Foundation Grant ESI 9553600. However, any opinions, findings, conclusions, statements, and recommendations expressed herein are those of the authors and do not necessarily reflect the views of the NSF.

Human Brain and Senses Resources
TABLE OF CONTENTS

Human Brain and Senses Resources
IMAGES

MRI OF THE OPTIC CHIASM

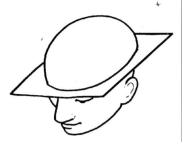

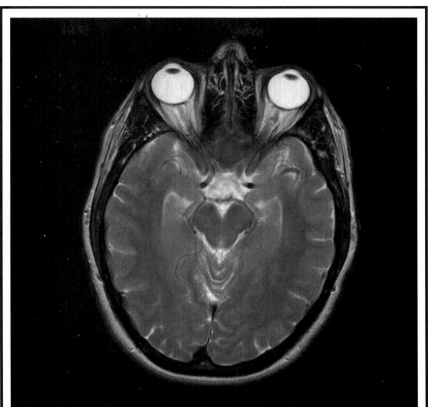

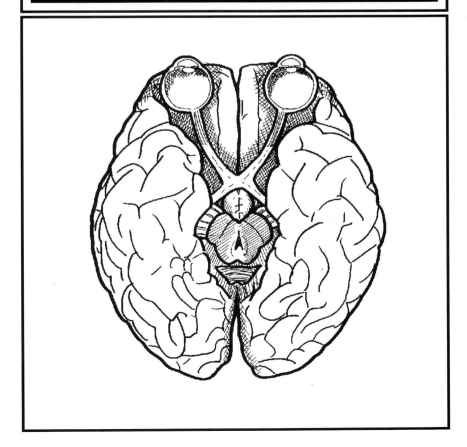

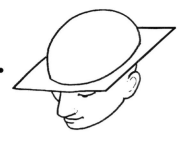

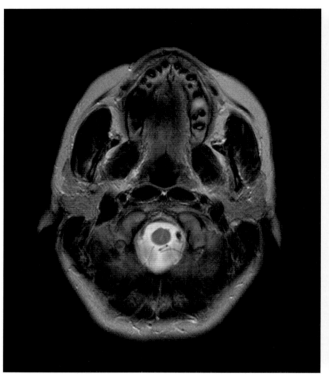

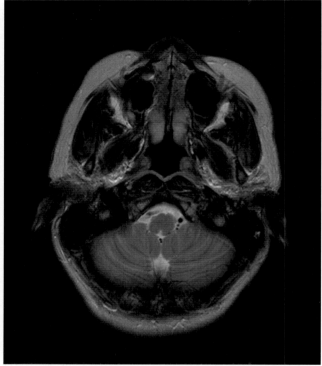

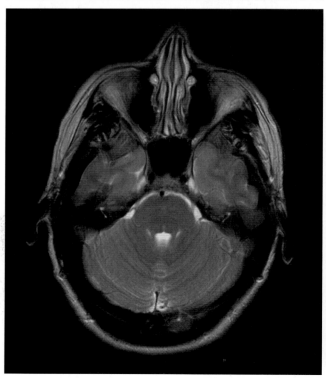

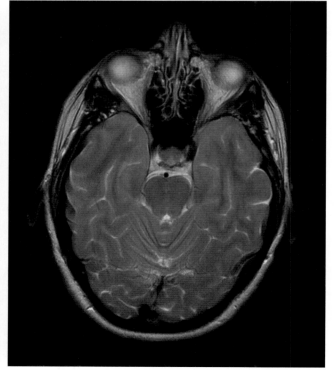

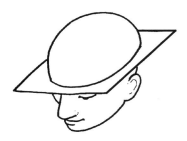

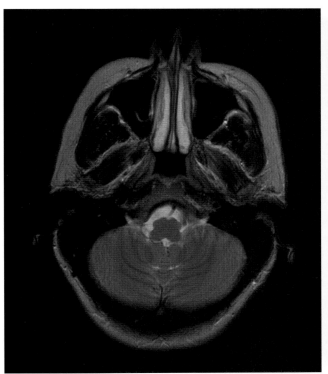 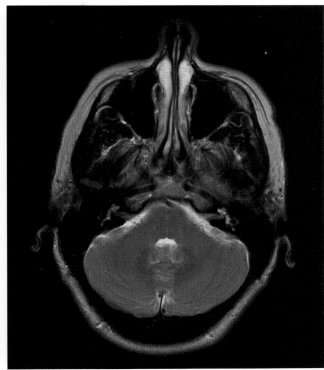

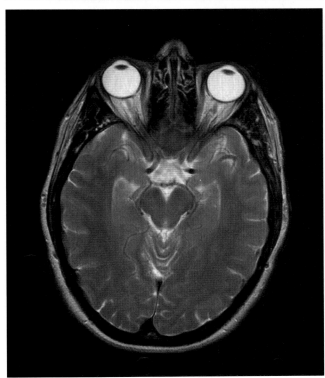 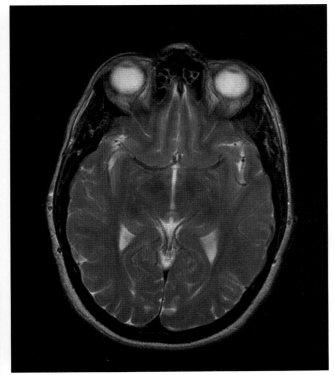

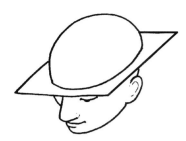

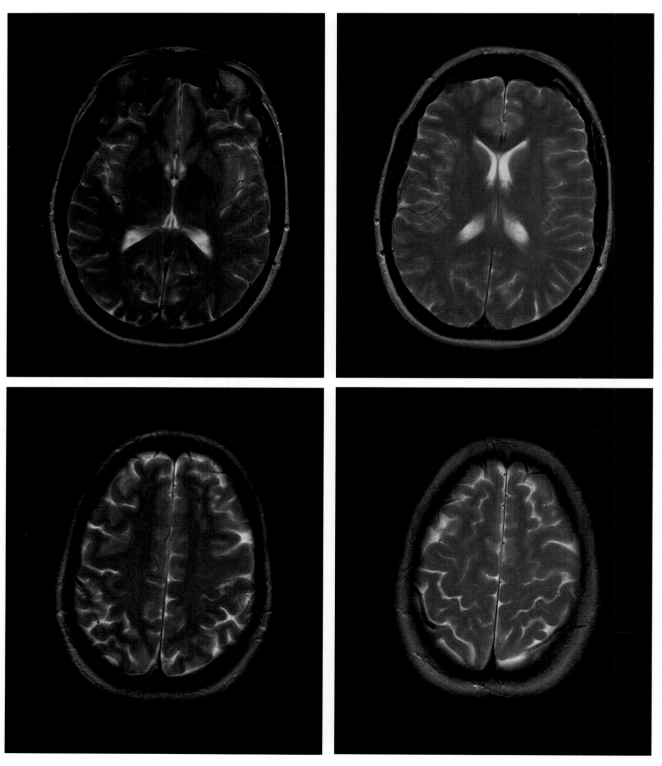

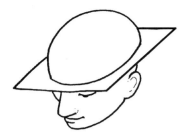

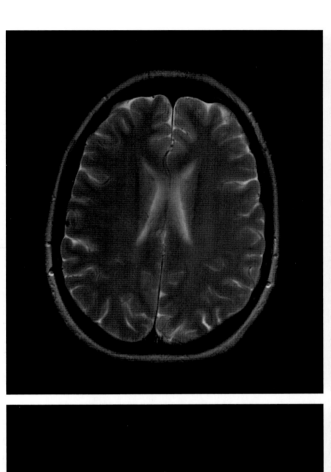

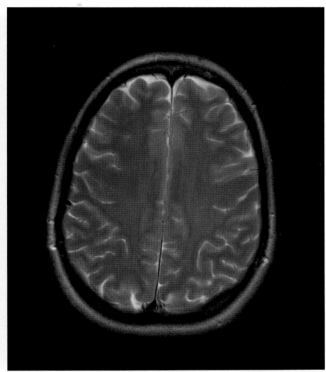

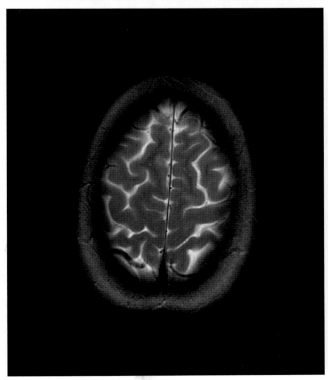

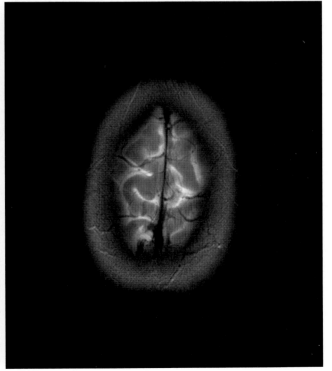

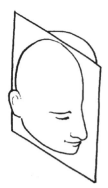

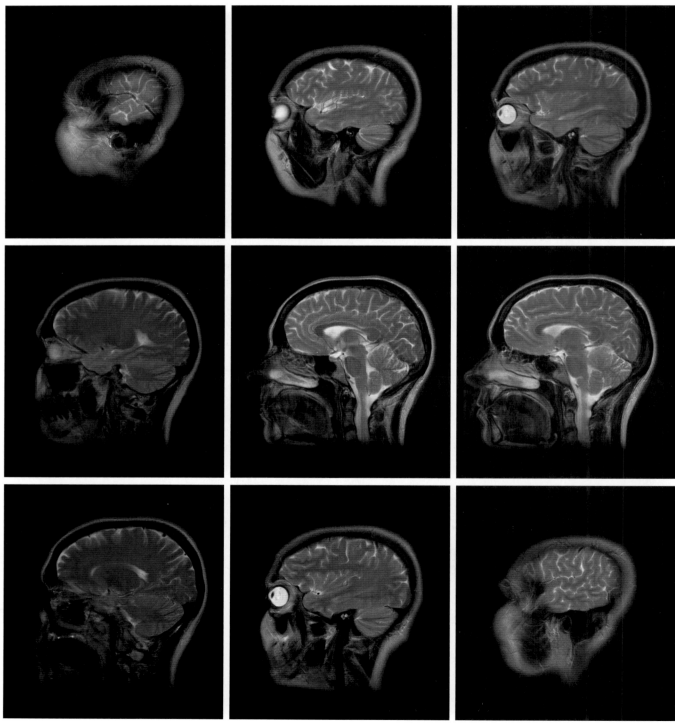

BRAIN ORIENTATION

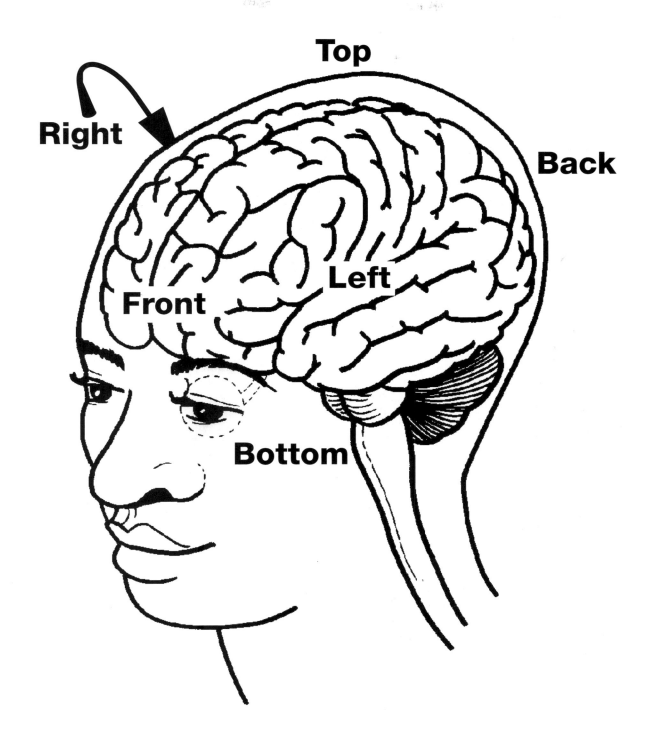

BRAIN-BOX IMAGE A

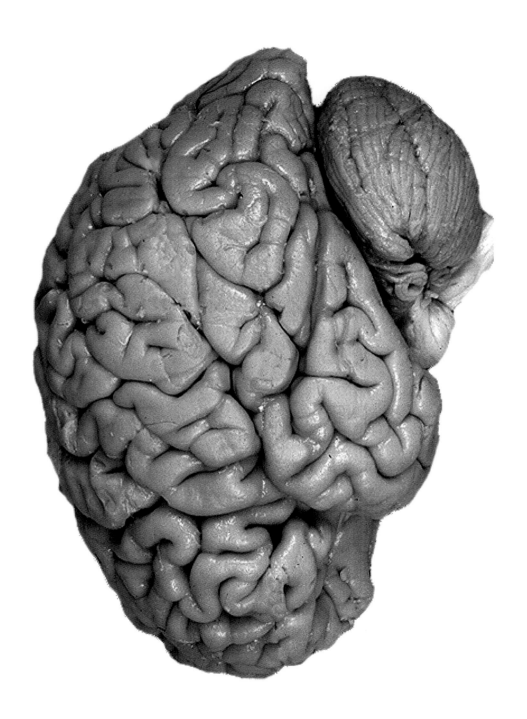

Image reproduced with permission from the Digital Anatomist Program, University of Washington.

BRAIN-BOX IMAGE B

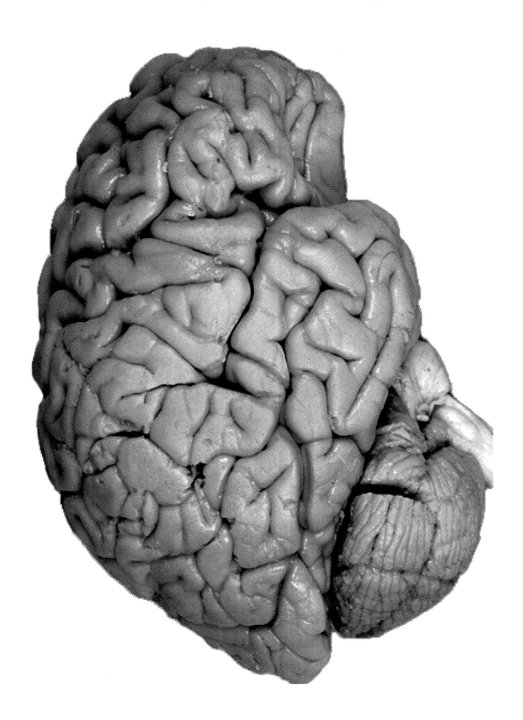

Image reproduced with permission from the Digital Anatomist Program, University of Washington.

BRAIN-BOX IMAGE C

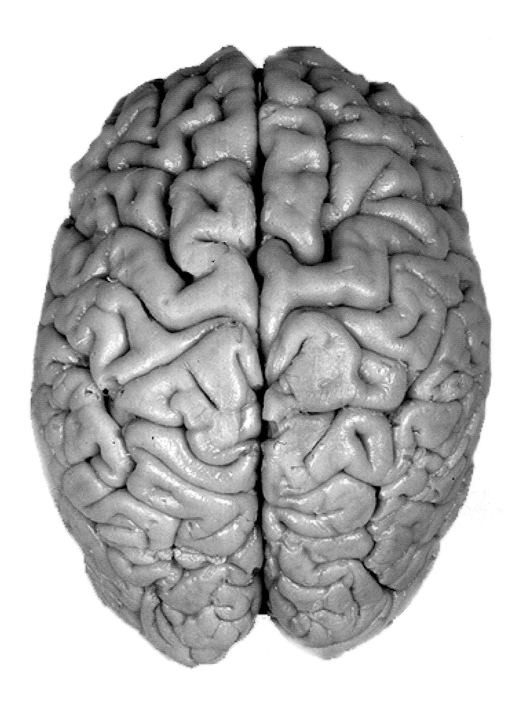

Image reproduced with permission from the Digital Anatomist Program, University of Washington.

BRAIN-BOX IMAGE D

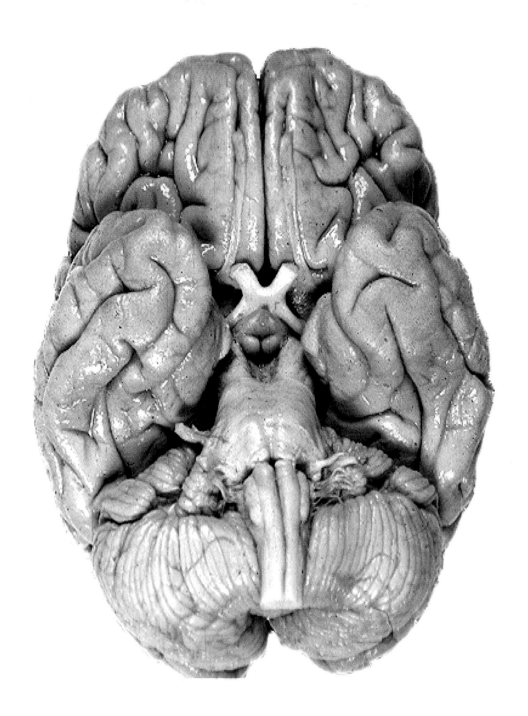

Image reproduced with permission from the Digital Anatomist Program, University of Washington.

BRAIN-BOX IMAGE E

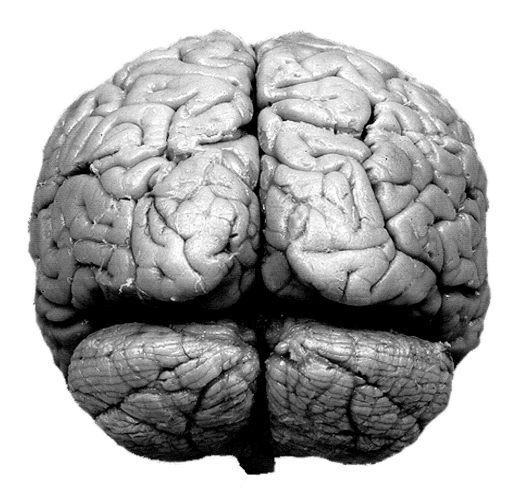

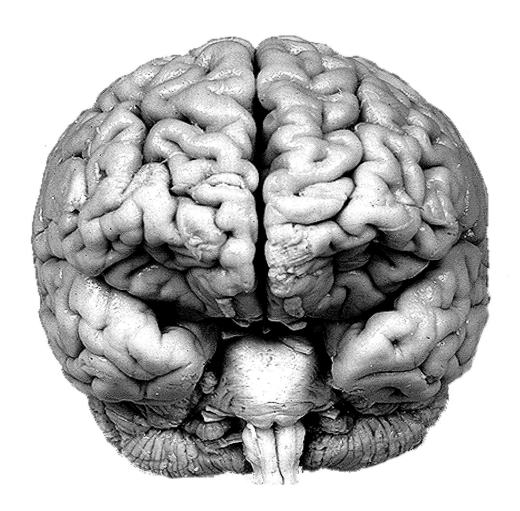

Image reproduced with permission from the Digital Anatomist Program, University of Washington.

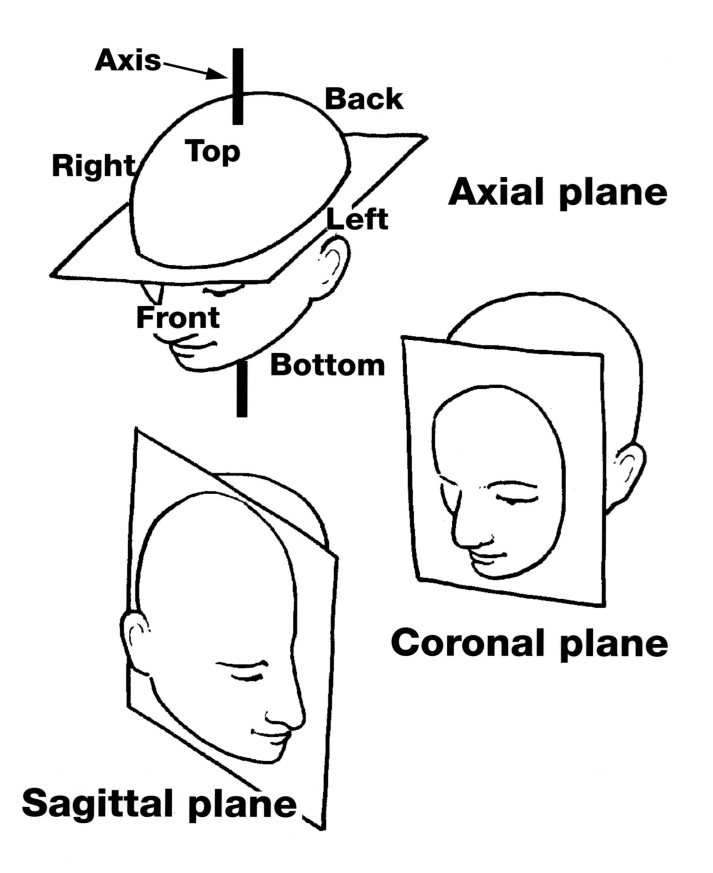

Axis

Back

Top

Right

Left

Axial plane

Front

Bottom

Coronal plane

Sagittal plane

Human Brain and Senses Resources
DATA

EEG GRAPHS FOR VISION

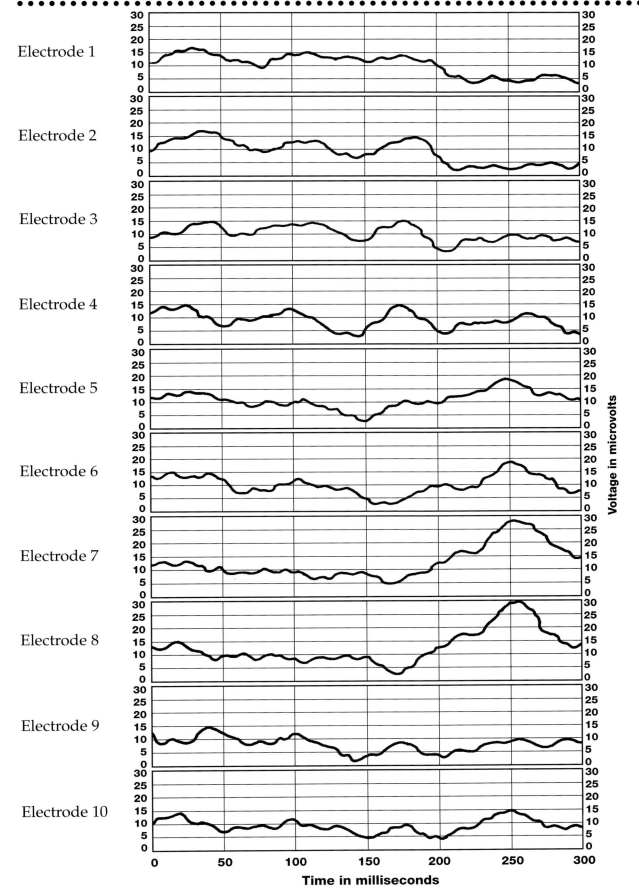

Electrode 1

Electrode 2

Electrode 3

Electrode 4

Electrode 5

Electrode 6

Electrode 7

Electrode 8

Electrode 9

Electrode 10

Voltage in microvolts

Time in milliseconds

EEG GRAPHS FOR TOUCH

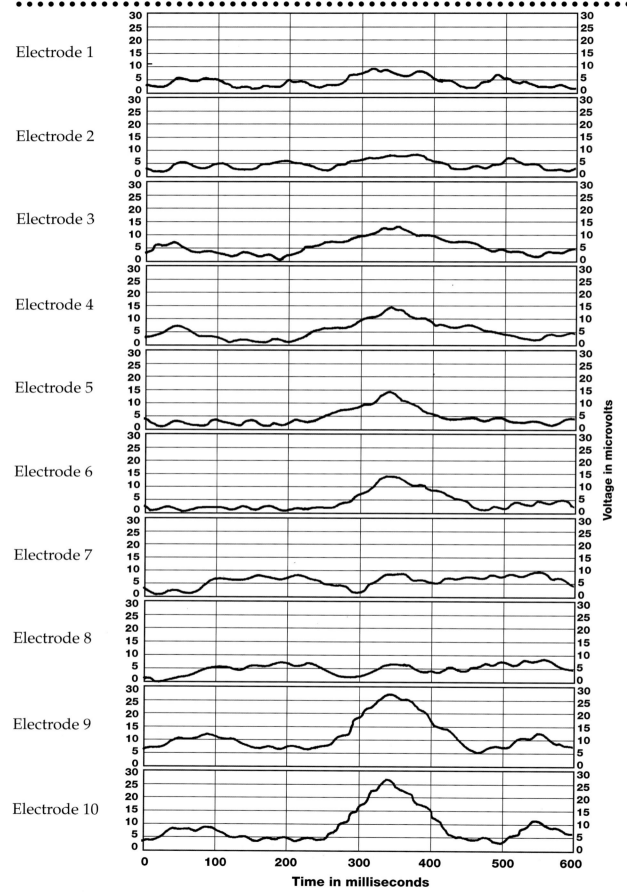

Human Brain and Senses Resources
READINGS

LEARNING AND MEMORY

Learning is defined as the acquisition of new knowledge and skills. **Memory** is the process of retrieving knowledge and bits of information related to skills that are stored in the brain. We depend on learning and memory every moment, in countless ways.

There are several different types of memory, including remembering visual images, such as faces; remembering facts; remembering events and experiences we had long ago; remembering how to do things, such as riding a bike or playing a musical instrument; and remembering smells, tastes, or feelings from the past. Each of these types of memory appears to be processed in the brain in a different way, and each is a vital part of everyday life.

LONG-TERM AND SHORT-TERM MEMORY

A classic case history illustrates the difference between long-term and short-term memory and suggested to scientists for the first time that the brain may process different types of memory in very different ways. A man with the initials H M developed a disease called epilepsy, which causes seizures, or brief spurts of uncoordinated brain activity, when he was 10 years old. As he grew older, the seizures became worse.

Finally it was decided that the only way to stop the seizures was to remove the part of H M's brain that was causing them. Surgeons took out the inner part of the temporal lobe on both hemispheres, including the cortex (surface), the amygdala, and most of the hippocampus.

After the operation H M seemed to be fine. His personality was the same. He could see, hear, feel, move, taste, and smell. He was just as intelligent as always.

However, he had trouble with his memory. While he could remember his childhood very well, he could not remember someone he met 5 minutes earlier. Dr. Brenda Milner, who worked with H M for more than 40 years, had to introduce herself to him every time she came into the room. When he was told to remember a number, he could do it for a very short time. When he was asked another question, he forgot not only the number, but being asked to remember it.

H M moved to a different house after his operation. Afterward, he couldn't remember how to find his way home, though he could find his old house easily. He always underestimated his age, and he could not recognize recent photographs of himself. He could remember things for very brief periods of time if he rehearsed them over and over in his mind, but as soon as he was distracted, he forgot them.

These memory patterns suggested to scientists that the part of the brain that processes short-term memory is in a different place than the part of the brain that stores long-term memory. Somehow the area of the cerebral cortex near the amygdala and hippocampus is responsible for transferring short-term memories into long-term storage. That part of H M's brain had been removed.

Scientists were surprised to find that the part of the brain that processes memory of fact or information (declarative memory) appears to be different from the part that processes physical skills (procedural memory). H M was able to learn new skills. For example, the doctors who worked with H M taught him to write by looking at his hand in a mirror, something that takes a lot of practice. He learned to do it fairly well, though he did not remember ever learning it or practicing it.

By studying H M and others with damage to different parts of the brain, scientists have learned about how the brain organizes and stores information, but much remains a mystery. We do know that memories seem to be synthesized from lots of bits that are stored in several different parts of the brain, and that the system is redundant, meaning that individual memories are not stored in one particular cell in the brain, as was once thought. Instead, memories seem to be a product of interaction between many different parts of the brain through a variety of pathways within the brain.

DECLARATIVE MEMORY

Learning facts and events is called **declarative memory.** Brain research suggests that there are several ways to reinforce this type of learning. For example, the more senses that process the information, the more likely the information will be remembered. If you read about something, talk about it out loud, write about it, see it, and touch it, you will probably remember it better than if you just hear someone tell you about it. Memories that are processed in several different places in the brain seem to have more chance of being accessed later.

Other brain research also has implications for how you learn. Practicing or repeating actions, thoughts, or speech physically changes the brain to make memories stronger. In addition, if your brain can associate new information with existing knowledge, you have a better chance of remembering that information. Also, if you associate strong emotion with the knowledge or the way in which you learned it, you are more likely to remember it.

You can use **mnemonic devices** to increase the effectiveness of declarative memory. For example, if you try to memorize a list of objects, one mnemonic device is to picture yourself walking through your house or town, putting these objects in particular locations. Then when asked to recall the list, you would take the same walk in your mind and "see" the objects.

Another mnemonic device that is useful for memorizing a list of things is to make up a phrase that has words that start with the same letters as the objects or concepts you are trying to remember. For example, to remember the notes that fall in the spaces of the treble clef, most piano students learn "**E**very **G**ood **B**oy **D**eserves **F**udge" or some variation of this phrase. When you learned the order of operations for mathematics, you might have used the phrase, "**M**y **D**ear **A**unt **S**ally," representing **m**ultiplication, **d**ivision, **a**ddition, and **s**ubtraction. Rhymes and songs are other common mnemonic devices. Most of us know the alphabet song, and many of us repeat "i before e, except after c" when thinking about how to spell words like *believe* or *receive*.

Helen Keller and Anne Sullivan

Helen Keller was born in 1880 in Alabama. When she was 19 months old, she had a fever that left her blind and deaf. Because Helen couldn't hear, she did not learn to speak, and it was nearly impossible for her to communicate with her family and the people around her. She became more and more difficult to live with. She knew that she was different from other people. Many times she would reach up to feel people's faces and find that their lips were moving. Their throats were vibrating. Helen could not understand what they were doing. She tried her best to imitate them, but could not seem to communicate. This left her very frustrated, and she often lashed out in anger, kicking and screaming until she was exhausted.

Her parents desperately visited many specialists trying to find help for Helen. By the time Helen was 6 years old, they had nearly given up, but they heard about Alexander Graham Bell, inventor of the telephone, who worked with deaf children. They went to visit him in Washington, DC, and he suggested that they write a letter to the Perkins Institute for the Blind in Boston. In 1887 the institute sent a young woman named Anne Sullivan to Alabama to be Helen's teacher.

Anne Sullivan, only 20 years old, had been blind herself as a child. She had several operations that allowed her to see, though not clearly. She was a determined and patient person, and she set out to teach Helen. At first it was very difficult to teach her anything, because Helen was used to getting her own way. Helen's family was not sure that it was even possible to teach a child who was blind and deaf. But slowly Anne Sullivan taught her, first to make letters by forming her fingers into a special alphabet, then to spell words. Anne would take a doll and let Helen hold it, then spell "d-o-l-l" into her other hand. Helen would spell the letters back to Anne. But it was just a game for Helen. She did not understand that the series of letters that Anne spelled into her hand meant the object in her other hand.

Anne was frustrated. She wanted to break through Helen's deafness and blindness somehow, to allow her to communicate and learn. She was convinced that Helen was very bright and that, if only she could understand that words stood for objects, Helen could learn many things. Anne spent many long hours spelling words into Helen's hand while handing her the objects in her other hand. It was hard for Helen too, because she sensed that her teacher was trying to tell her something, and she simply could not understand what it was.

One day Helen was tired of the game, and she threw the doll to the ground in frustration, breaking it to pieces. Anne took her out of the house, also tired of trying to make Helen understand. They came to a well, and Anne started to pump water over Helen's hands. Sighing, she spelled "w-a-t-e-r" into Helen's other hand, as she had done countless times before. But this time was different. Helen suddenly stood still, completely focused on what her teacher was doing. She grabbed Anne's hand, excitedly spelling "w-a-t-e-r" back, and then splashing the water. Back and forth, back and forth, she repeated the movements, more and more animated. Anne felt like laughing and crying at the same time—she knew Helen finally understood that the word water meant this cool, refreshing wet stuff that was splashing over her hands and face.

Helen ran from the water pump and began pointing to things, asking for the names. All the days of spelling into her hand suddenly made sense for Helen as she finally connected the series of finger movements with the things that surrounded her. "Tree" and "ground" and "flower" came to life. When they came back into the house, Helen ran to find her parents. She pointed to them, and Anne spelled "mother" and "father" as Helen learned these words for the first time. Then, shyly, Helen crept over to Anne and pointed to her. "Teacher," spelled Anne. "Teacher," spelled Helen, and that was what she called Anne Sullivan for the rest of her life.

Anne taught Helen many things, and they stayed together from then on. She learned to read and write Braille, a system of writing for the blind that uses raised dots. By the time she was 16, Helen learned to speak by imitating the vibrations and lip movements of her teacher. She was hard to understand, but she could speak. She also learned to lip-read by placing her fingers on the lips of people as they talked.

Helen was tutored in high school classes, and she went to Radcliffe College, which was the women's college at Harvard University. It was difficult for her to keep up with her classes, because she had to have Anne spell out everything that her teachers said. Many of the books she needed were not available in Braille, so Anne had to read them and then spell everything to Helen. It was hard work for Anne Sullivan as well as for Helen Keller! Despite these difficulties, Helen graduated with honors in 1904.

For the rest of her life, Helen helped others with physical disabilities. She traveled all around the United States and to other countries, and wrote many books. She wrote articles for magazines about blindness, she helped organize 30 state commissions for the blind, and she supported the American Foundation for the Blind. All her life she loved books and reading, and she helped open libraries for children around the country. Her amazing success was an inspiration for others. She met many famous people, including Alexander Graham Bell, the poets Oliver Wendell Holmes and John Greenleaf Whittier, and several presidents of the United States. In 1962 the story of Anne Sullivan and Helen Keller was made into an Oscar-winning movie, *The Miracle Worker.* The next year Helen Keller was awarded the Presidential Medal of Freedom. She died in 1968.

To learn more about Helen Keller and Anne Sullivan, try these resources.

Books

The Story of My Life by Helen Keller

Light in My Darkness by Helen Keller

Teacher: Anne Sullivan Macy by Helen Keller

Helen Keller and Anne Sullivan: Working Miracles Together by Jon Zonderman

Helen and Teacher: The Story of Helen Keller and Anne Sullivan Macy by Joseph Lash

Videos

The Miracle Worker, starring Anne Bancroft and Patty Duke

Helen Keller, American Women of Achievement Video Collection

Chapter 4

The most important day I remember in all my life is the one on which my teacher, Anne Mansfield Sullivan, came to me. I am filled with wonder when I consider the immeasurable contrasts between the two lives which it connects. It was the third of March, 1887, three months before I was seven years old.

On the afternoon of that eventful day, I stood on the porch, dumb, expectant. I guessed vaguely from my mother's signs and from the hurrying to and from in the house that something unusual was about to happen, so I went to the door and waited on the steps. The afternoon sun penetrated the mass of honeysuckle that covered the porch, and fell on my upturned face. My fingers lingered almost unconsciously on the familiar leaves and blossoms which had just come forth to greet the sweet southern spring. I did not know what the future held of marvel or purpose for me. Anger and bitterness had preyed upon me continually for weeks and a deep languor had succeeded this passionate struggle.

Have you even been at sea in a dense fog, when it seemed as if a tangible white darkness shut you in, and the great ship, tense and anxious, groped her way toward the shore with plummet and sounding-line,

and you waited with beating heart for something to happen? I was like that ship before my education began, only I was without compass or sounding-line and had no way of knowing how near the harbour was. "Light! Give me light!" was the wordless cry of my soul, and the light of love shone on me in that very hour.

I felt approaching footsteps. I stretched out my hand as I supposed to my mother. Some one took it, and I was caught up and held close in the arms of her who had come to reveal all things to me, and, more than all things else, to love me.

The morning after my teacher came she led me into her room and gave me a doll. The little blind children at the Perkins Institution had sent it, and Laura Bridgman had dressed it; but I did not know this until afterward. When I had played with it a little while, Miss Sullivan slowly spelled into my hand the word "d-o-l-l." I was at once interested in this finger play and tried to imitate it. When I finally succeeded in making the letters correctly I was flushed with childish pleasure and pride. Running downstairs to my mother I held up my hand and made the letter for doll. I did not know that I was spelling a word or even that words existed; I was simply making my fingers go in monkey-like imitation. In the days that followed I learned to spell in this uncomprehending way a great many words, among them pin, hat, cup and a few verbs like sit, stand, and walk. But my teacher had been with me several weeks before I understood that everything has a name.

One day, while I was playing with my new doll, Miss Sullivan put my big rag doll into my lap also, spelled "d-o-l-l" and tried to make me understand that "d-o-l-l" applied to both. Earlier in the day we had had a tussle over the words "m-u-g" and "w-a-t-e-r." Miss Sullivan had tried to impress upon me that "m-u-g" is mug and that "w-a-t-e-r" is water, but I persisted in confounding the two. In despair she had dropped the subject for the time, only to renew it at the first opportunity. I became impatient at her repeated attempts and, seizing the new doll, I dashed it upon the floor. I was keenly delighted when I felt the fragments of the broken doll at my feet. Neither sorrow nor regret followed my passionate outburst. I had not loved the doll. In the still, dark world in which I lived there was no strong sentiment or tenderness. I felt my teacher sweep the fragments to one side of the hearth and I had a sense of satisfaction that the cause of my discomfort was removed. She brought me my hat, and I knew I was going out into the warm sunshine. This thought, if a wordless sensation may be called a thought, made me hop and skip with pleasure.

We walked down the path to the well-house, attracted by the fragrance of the honeysuckle with which it was covered. Someone was drawing water and my

teacher placed my hand under the spout. As the cool stream gushed over one hand she spelled into the other the word *water,* first slowly, then rapidly. I stood still, my whole attention fixed upon the motions of her fingers. Suddenly I felt a misty consciousness as of something forgotten—a thrill of returning thought; and somehow the mystery of language was revealed to me. I knew then that "w-a-t-e-r" meant the wonderful cool something that was flowing over my hand. That living word awakened my soul, gave it light, hope, joy, set it free! There were barriers still, it is true, but barriers that could in time be swept away.

I left the well-house eager to learn. Everything had a name, and each name gave birth to a new thought. As we returned to the house every object which I touched seemed to quiver with life. That was because I saw everything with the strange, new sight that had come to me. On entering the door I remembered the doll I had broken. I felt my way to the hearth and picked up the pieces. I tried vainly to put them together. Then my eyes filled with tears; for I realized what I had done, and for the first time I felt repentance and sorrow.

I learned a great many new words that day. I do not remember what they all were; but I do know that mother, father, sister, teacher were among them—words that were to make the world blossom for me, "like Aaron's rod, with flowers." It would have been difficult to find a happier child than I was as I lay in my crib at the close of that eventful day and lived over the joys it had brought me, and for the first time longed for a new day to come.

THE MAMMALIAN EYE

Mammals have much in common, including the way their eyes work. Within the mammalian eye are several structures that make it the most complex and sophisticated visual sense organ of the animal kingdom. Let's consider what those structures are and how they work together to allow mammals to see.

The eye is protected by the bony orbit in which it sits, as well as by the eyebrows, eyelashes, and eyelids that keep dirt, sweat, and other foreign material out. Each eye has six muscles attached to the outside of the sclera: two muscles to move the eye left and right, and four to move it up and down. These muscles are surrounded by fat, which helps cushion the eye in the event of a blow to the eye or head.

The **pupil** is the dark circular opening in the center of the iris. A close examination of the **iris** reveals that it is highly textured and often made up of several colors. The color of the iris depends on the amount of pigmentation in it; the more there is, the darker the iris is. Irises have no blue or green; light-colored eyes result from the lack of the same pigment (melanin) that is in brown eyes. The iris is made up of a series of circular muscles that constrict to make the pupil smaller in bright light and radiating muscles that constrict to make the pupil larger in dim light.

The pupil and iris lie behind the bulging transparent covering of the eye, the **cornea,** which is most easily observed from the side. The cornea has no blood vessels; it is maintained by the fluid behind it, the **aqueous humor,** and by tears on its surface. Tears are produced by the **lacrimal gland** and are constantly secreted onto the front of the eye via small openings hidden on the back side of the upper eyelid. Tears exit the eye through a similar opening on the lower lid, draining into the nasal cavity. (This is the reason that your nose runs when you cry.) In the disease

Optic nerve
Optic disk (blind spot)
Retina
Ciliary muscles
Lens
Muscle
Macula
Fovea
Sclera

glaucoma, the aqueous humor builds up to dangerous levels, causing too much pressure on the eye.

The cornea is continuous with the white of the eye, the **sclera,** which is the tough covering that surrounds the entire eyeball and helps it maintain its shape. Running throughout the sclera are tiny **blood vessels** that provide nourishment and oxygen. Red eyes result from irritation of these blood vessels.

Behind the iris is the **lens,** a clear convex disk held in place by a ring of delicate fibers called the **ciliary muscles.** The cornea and lens focus the light that comes into the eye. The curved surface of the cornea and the fluid behind it act as the main lens for focusing an image. The main role of the lens in the eye is to make slight adjustments in focus as you look at something far away and then something close-up. This adjustment in focus is called accommodation and is controlled by the ciliary muscles. The lens hardens as a person ages, until it can no longer respond to the ciliary muscles in order to create a focused image of an object that is close to the eye. This hardening is why many people need reading glasses or bifocals as they age.

Most of the inside of the eye contains a clear jellylike sphere called the **vitreous humor.** This sphere holds the internal structures of the eye in place and maintains the shape of the eye.

Along the back of the inside of the eye is a thin translucent layer of tissue called the **retina.** When an image forms on the retina, a message travels to the brain for processing. The pupil appears dark because of the light-absorbing pigments on the retina. When flash photography is used, pupils often appear red because of the reflection of the bright flash off blood vessels in the retina. Cameras with red-eye reduction release one or more bright flashes of light just before the picture is taken. The bright light causes the pupils of the people in the picture to constrict, reducing the amount of light that reflects off the retina.

Cow eyes are like human eyes, with a few exceptions. The pupils are shaped differently—round in humans, oval in cows. Cows also have a shiny blue-green layer, the **tapetum,** lining the eye behind the retina. This layer, not present in humans, helps cows to see better at night. The tapetum reflects light so that it passes through the retina twice. The bright, reflective eye shine of cats, wolves, lions, and other nocturnal animals is light reflected back from the tapetum.

LENSES and LIGHT

How do we see something? The ancient Greeks thought that the eyes sent out invisible rays that allowed a person to perceive objects. They theorized that vision took place out in space, since objects appeared to be outside of a person's body.

In 1625 a priest named Christopher Scheiner who was investigating vision had the idea of carefully scraping the opaque sclera off the back of an eye. When he aimed the eye at a brightly lit scene, he saw a small, inverted, reversed image appear on the back of the eye.

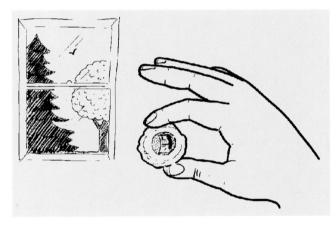

This landmark experiment demonstrated that vision happened within the eye rather than out in space. That's how eyes work—they collect light from the environment and focus that light as an image on the back surface of the eye.

For an object to be visible, it must either produce light or reflect light. Objects such as the Sun, a candle flame, and a lightbulb produce their own light; objects such as the Moon, a candlestick, and people reflect light.

BENDING LIGHT

Light travels through transparent media, like air, water, and glass, in a straight line as long as the composition of the medium remains constant. However, when it enters a transparent medium that has a different composition, light bends at the point of contact between the two media. This bending is called **refraction,** and every transparent medium has an index of refraction that indicates the degree to which light will bend. Light bends the most when the difference between the indices of refraction is highest.

The amount of refraction also depends on the angle at which the light hits the new medium, called the **angle of incidence.** If light hits straight on, perpendicular to the surface, it does not bend. As the angle of incidence increases, the light bends more. These two factors—the index of refraction of the medium, and the angle of incidence at which light hits it—determine the amount of refraction, called the **angle of refraction.**

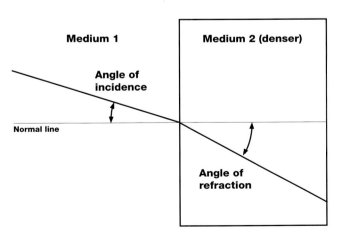

LENSES

A **lens** is a clear, curved object that has a different index of refraction than its surrounding medium. The curvature of the surface of the lens bends light rays at different angles. When light passes through, it bends or refracts to bring all of the rays of light together at one point. This point is called a **focus.** Light rays coming in parallel to one another will be refracted by a lens and will converge at a point known as the **principal focus,** or **focal length,** for that lens.

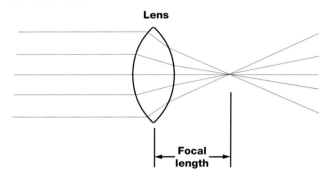

When the light rays come together to focus, they form an **image.** If light passing through a convex lens bends or refracts to form an image on a surface, that image is projected. A **projected image** is always inverted and reversed because the light rays cross each other.

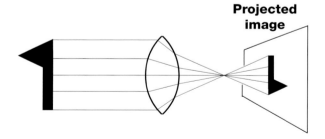

Notice on the diagram that the parallel rays of light go through the lens, bend at different angles, and cross each other to form a projected image on the screen. The diagram is misleading, however, because it suggests that all rays of light from an object cross at the same point. This is not true. Each point of the object is actually reflecting hundreds of rays of light in all different directions. In the diagram

below, we see what happens to six of those rays of light leaving two points of the object. They pass through the lens, refract, and meet again to form the image. They do not, however, cross at the same point.

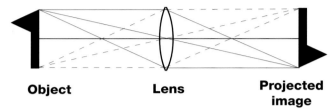

If you could draw a diagram that showed all the rays of light, it would be very hard to follow one ray. Even though the diagrams we use have only a few rays of light drawn on them, you should remember that many more rays make up an image.

Notice also that when a ray of light hits the center of the lens, it appears to continue straight through. This is not exactly correct—in fact, the rays refract one way when they enter the lens, and then back exactly to their original angle when they leave the lens. The only ray of light that does not bend at all is one that hits the very center of the lens exactly perpendicular to the lens surface.

In the case of the eye, the image projected onto the screen is smaller than the actual object. This allows the image to fit inside the eyeball. The image focuses on the retina and travels to the brain. The brain interprets the image so that we see the object in its correct orientation.

In the vertebrate eye are two lenses, the cornea and the lens itself. The curved surface of the cornea and the fluid behind it act as the main lens for focusing an image in the eyes of land vertebrates. This is because light bends a lot more going from air to cornea and aqueous humor (very different indexes of refraction) than it does going from aqueous humor to the lens (very similar indexes of refraction).

This difference in refraction is obvious when you try to see underwater—once the cornea is surrounded by water instead of air, the difference between the indexes of refraction is much less and therefore your vision is out of focus. If you put on a diver's mask, the air between the eye and the view in the environment has a different index of refraction, so the image is once again in focus.

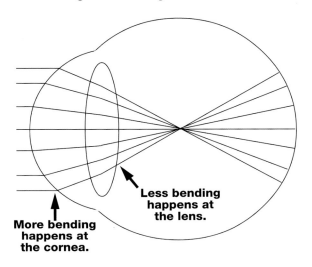

Less bending happens at the lens.

More bending happens at the cornea.

The distance between the lens and the screen on which a projected image is focused is called the **image focus distance.** This distance is not necessarily the same as the principal focus of a lens because most of the light rays that enter our eyes are not all parallel to one another. Light rays from distant objects are parallel to one another and they form an image closer to the lens. Light rays from close objects come in at angles and form an image farther from the lens.

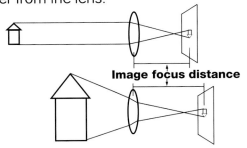

Image focus distance

Focus distance can be changed by changing the curvature of the lens. Increasing the curvature of the lens decreases focus distance.

Using two lenses together changes the focus distance. In the human eye the cornea and lens together give an image focus distance of about 2.5 cm (1 inch), which is the diameter of the eyeball. When the eye is not able to focus the image right on the back of the eye, it is necessary to add another lens to the vision system. Eyeglasses are lenses placed in front of the eye to make the image focus in exactly the right place.

THE CAMERA AND THE EYE

Nearly a thousand years ago, Arabian scientists discovered that they could create an image on the wall of a darkened room if they made a small hole in one wall, which acted as a lens. This projection is known as a **camera obscura** (Latin for "darkened room").

Centuries later the same principle was used to develop the photographic camera. A tiny hole or a glass lens focuses light from a scene onto the back of a darkened box. By placing a plate of glass or cellulose coated with light-sensitive emulsion in the camera where the image forms, the image can be captured. The emulsion reacts to light—the brighter the light, the faster the reaction takes place. Back in the photographic lab the photographer treats the exposed plate with a set of chemicals that wash away the portions of the emulsion that were not bombarded by light. The emulsion on the glass plate forms a permanent image of the scene.

A camera is like an eye in many ways. Both have a lens that allows light into a darkened container and focuses an image on the back. In a camera the screen is the film with the light-sensitive emulsion, and this reacts with light to form a permanent record of the focused image. In an eye, the light-sensitive emulsion is replaced by light-sensitive living tissue, the retina, which serves as the screen for the projected image. This image information travels to the brain for processing.

Corrective Lenses

About a third of us need to wear corrective lenses, either glasses or contact lenses, to allow us to see clearly. The three most common conditions corrective lenses can solve are **MYopia** (nearsightedness), **hyperopia** (farsightedness), and **astigmatism.**

MYOPIA

In **myopia** the cornea is too curved, or the eyeball is longer than the focal length of the cornea and lens. The projected image focuses in front of the retina. To correct this, a person must add another lens. A concave lens spreads the light rays out slightly, so that the cornea and lens will focus the image on the retina.

HYPEROPIA

In **hyperopia** the cornea is too flat, or the eyeball is shorter than the focal length of the cornea and lens. The image focuses in back of the retina. To correct this, a person must add a convex lens. This lens makes the light rays converge a bit more before they enter the eye to be focused by the cornea and lens.

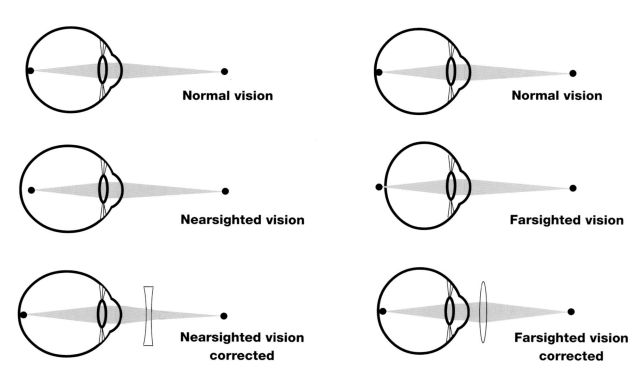

Normal vision

Nearsighted vision

Nearsighted vision corrected

Normal vision

Farsighted vision

Farsighted vision corrected

ASTIGMATISM

The cornea is the most powerful lens in the eye. If the surface of the cornea is not perfectly smooth or curved in exactly the same way in all angles, it can cause irregularities in the focus of light rays, which results in a distorted image. Nearly all people have some irregularity in the surface of the cornea, known as an **astigmatism.** To correct this condition, people wear lenses that have a similar but opposite irregularity in focus, resulting in a properly focused image.

LASER SURGERY

In some cases a person may choose to have surgery to correct myopia, hyperopia, or astigmatism, rather than wearing corrective lenses. In laser surgery a laser shaves off small amounts of the cornea to reshape the curvature so that it will focus correctly. Lasers are so precise that they can take off single cells at a time, which allows very specific corrections to be made on the cornea.

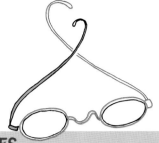

READING GLASSES

No matter what sort of vision you have when you are young, chances are that you will one day need glasses to help you see things that are close to you. The lens inside your eye is mostly used to focus on close objects. The lens stretches to change shape, allowing the focus to change.

As you age, however, your lens hardens. Sometime in your 40s your lens will no longer be able to change shape to help you see things that are close up. By your mid-40s you will probably need to use reading glasses or bifocals, even if your vision was perfect until then.

The Retina

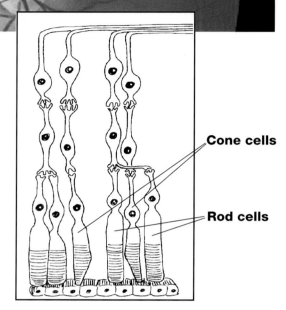

Cone cells

Rod cells

The precise organization of the structures in the eye is dedicated to one important function: to focus an image on the retina. The retina, the curved screen at the back of the eye, is where light energy changes into electric impulses that travel to the brain for processing. But how does this happen?

The Photoreceptors

The retina is actually an extension of the brain itself. When photons of light reach the retina, they pass through two layers of cells before hitting a dense layer of the specialized light-sensitive cells that transform light energy into electric impulses.

There are two types of photoreceptors. The **rods,** which are long and skinny, are sensitive to dim light and do not respond to bright light. Rods cannot detect colors. The **cones,** which are triangular, are not responsive in dim light but

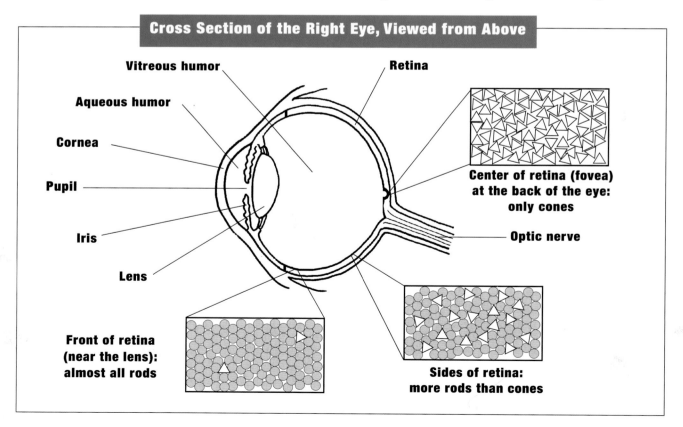

Cross Section of the Right Eye, Viewed from Above

Vitreous humor

Aqueous humor

Cornea

Pupil

Iris

Lens

Retina

Center of retina (fovea) at the back of the eye: only cones

Optic nerve

Front of retina (near the lens): almost all rods

Sides of retina: more rods than cones

respond to bright light. Cones distinguish color and detect fine details of objects.

Three different types of cones are in the human retina, each responding to a different color of light—red, green, and blue. A malfunction of one or more of the kinds of cone cells results in color blindness.

Approximately 125 million rods and 6 million cones are in a typical human eye. Yet we experience our world as being full of detail and color. How can this be true if our eyes have so many more rods than cones?

The Structure of the Retina

When an optometrist puts drops in your eyes to dilate your pupils, and shines light into your eyes, it's your retina that is being inspected. From this view your retina looks reddish orange and is webbed with blood vessels.

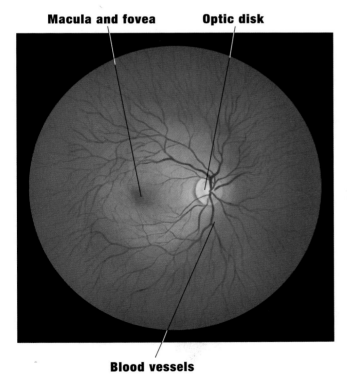

Macula and fovea **Optic disk**

Blood vessels

There are two contrasting spots on your retina. The dark red **macula** (literally "spot") has a high concentration of cone cells—in fact, just about all of the eye's cone cells—and relatively few blood vessels. In the center of the macula is a small depression called the **fovea** (literally "pit"), which contains *only* cone cells. The fovea is the area of the retina that has the highest sensitivity to color and detail, because cone cells are packed together more densely here than in any other part of the retina. The fovea is depressed because the layers of cells through which light normally must pass before getting to the receptor cells are pushed to the side here. The fovea is where an image focuses when you look directly at an object.

The larger, lighter-colored spot called the **optic disk** is where the optic nerve attaches to the back of the eye. The optic disk has no photoreceptors at all, so is a blind spot in the field of vision of each eye.

The blind spot was not discovered until the 1700s, relatively late in visual science, because the area of each eye's blind spot is within the visual field of the other eye. Because the brain fills in missing details, it is difficult to locate the blind spot while looking at a large object or one that blends in with the background.

Several large blood vessels radiate from the optic disk to nourish the living tissue of the retina. These blood vessels block light from reaching the photoreceptors beneath them, thus creating more blind areas. You can demonstrate this by entering a darkened room and shining a flashlight into one of your eyes. While holding the other eye closed, if you move your eye around and jiggle the flashlight, you will probably be able to see a dark treelike structure against the wall. The tree is a negative image of the blood vessels in your eye. The pattern of blood vessels across the retina is as distinctive as a fingerprint, and retinal scans of this pattern are used to identify people in certain high-security fields.

Macular Damage

When cones are subjected to light that is too intense, they can be permanently damaged. Careless activities like looking at arc welding or gazing directly into the Sun can destroy the cone cells in the macula and fovea. When this happens, as it frequently did to astronomers and navigators in past centuries, the person loses vision in the center of the visual field.

Remember that the center is where we see color and detail. To simulate what it would be like to lose vision in your macula, hold your arm out straight in front of you and make a fist. Focus on that fist as you try to walk or look around. Keep looking at your fist! Notice that you would not be able to read, recognize faces, or do anything else that would require making out detail, because the area of your retina with the highest concentration of cone cells is damaged.

What you can see with both eyes wide open is your **field of vision.** It is typically about 180°, or a half circle out in front from side to side, and about 120° up and down. Your eyebrow ridge and cheekbones reduce your vertical field of vision, so the field is a little less than a hemisphere.

Here is a cross-section view of your right eye as seen from above. The lines represent different light rays entering through the center of the eye's lens system.

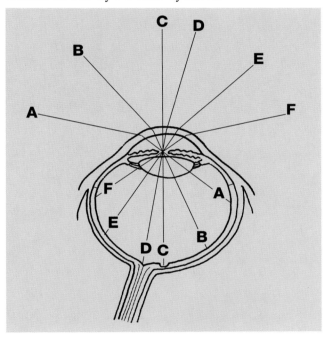

In the illustration you can see that light coming from the edges of the field of vision (A and F) hits the retina well away from the center. This part of the retina is populated almost exclusively by rods, and rods provide poorly resolved images in shades of gray. Consequently, vision off to the sides and at the top and bottom of your visual fields, known as **peripheral vision,** provides you mostly with contrast and motion information. You do not get much color and detail information from your peripheral vision.

The rays that enter your eyes halfway between the periphery of your visual field and straight ahead (B and E) fall on the intermediate regions of the retina. In this region the retina still has mostly rods, but there are some cones as well. In this area of the visual field, you can see color if the light is intense, but the images will still be poorly resolved because there are few cones.

When you look right at something (C), the light falls on the center of the retina, the macula, which contains mostly cones. This part of your visual field gives you good color vision and good resolution. At the center of the macula is the fovea, the indentation that contains only cones. You use this part of the retina when you read, look closely at details, and study subtle differences in colors. When you look at something, you usually turn your head and move your eyes to position its image right on the fovea, so that you can see it clearly.

And finally light ray D falls right on the optic disk. Because there are no receptors, neither rods nor cones, on the optic disk, the retina is blind at this location. Unless you intentionally try to locate your blind spots, however, you are never aware of them, because the blind spots fall into the region of binocular vision, or the portion of your field of vision seen by both eyes at the same time. Missing information in one eye is simply filled in by the brain.

THE LARGE EYES OF BIRDS ARE ILLUSTRATED BY THIS GREAT HORNED OWL.

WHEN IT COMES TO KEEN VISION, THE BIRD'S EYE IS A SIGHT TO BEHOLD

THE EYES HAVE IT

BY ELDON GREIJ

Eyes are remarkable structures that have reached their highest development in birds. First of all, bird eyes are huge—proportionately much larger than human eyes—and can be as large as their brain. The large pupil (the opening in front of the eye through which light passes) significantly increases the amount of light that enters. It is this factor that allows birds to "see" in much lower light than humans can see. Birds that are active at dawn and dusk (crepuscular), such as nighthawks, poorwills, and owls, have the largest eyes. In contrast, the nocturnal kiwis of New Zealand, which rely on their unusually good sense of smell to locate earthworms, have very small eyes.

For most birds, the eyes' large size causes them to bulge into the center of the head where they almost touch, forcing the brain to be shifted backwards (see illustration, next page).

An American robin tilts its head to get a better view of an earthworm in the grass.

They are crammed into their opening in the skull (orbits) so tightly that little or no movement is possible, even though they have the same six muscles for moving the eyes that we have.

Consequently, birds have very mobile heads. According to one macabre legend, if you walk all the way around an owl repeatedly, it will follow you with its eyes until its head falls off. Fortunately, that's not so. Owls are the champion head-turners, however, and are able to rotate their heads as much as 270 degrees. Birds turn their head to look at objects, where we would simply move our eyes. This is evident in the common myth that robins, when cocking their heads toward the grass, are listening for earthworms. In reality, they are tilting their heads to direct the image onto the most sensitive part of the retina.

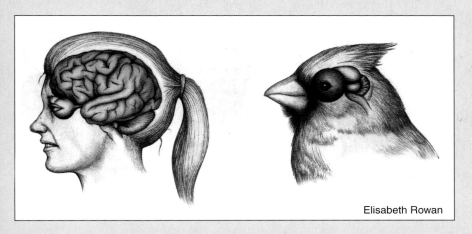
Elisabeth Rowan

RELATIVE TO THE SIZE OF THE BRAIN, THE BIRD EYE IS MUCH LARGER THAN THE HUMAN EYE. THE LARGE SIZE OF THE BIRD'S EYE SOCKETS FORCES THE BRAIN TO OCCUPY A SPACE FARTHER BACK IN THE SKULL.

Like the human eye, sensory cells (rods and cones) that respond to light are packed into the retina, a layer that lines the inside of the eye behind the lens. Unlike the human eye, the avian retina has many more sensory cells—probably three times as many—per unit area, which gives birds much greater visual acuity than humans, and explains why hawks can see a mouse at a much greater distance than we can. Like humans, the sensory cells of bird eyes consist of rods, which see only black and white but are stimulated in less light, and cones, which permit color vision, but require more light for stimulation. An unusual feature of avian cones is the presence of oil droplets. These droplets are red, orange, yellow, and green in diurnal birds and colorless to dull yellow in nocturnal birds. While the function of these droplets is not known, they are thought to improve vision by acting as filters to penetrate haze, enhancing color vision by filtering certain wavelengths of light, or allowing certain colors to be more visible.

The area of the retina that provides the greatest visual acuity is called the fovea; it contains the highest concentration of sensory cells. For example, as you read these words, the images are being focused on your fovea. While mammals, including humans, have a single fovea, some birds have two or three. These multiple areas of sharp vision are especially valuable for birds that need great visual acuity, such as swallows and raptors that pursue elusive prey on the wing.

Because the sensory cells (rods and cones) in the retina have a high metabolism, they require a constant supply of oxygen and nutrients. While the human retina contains a network of blood vessels to distribute these essential materials, the bird retina does not. Perhaps blood vessels would interfere with the much higher concentration of sensory cells and keener vision of birds. Instead, birds have a large vascular structure with accordion-like folds, called a pecten, which protrudes from the back of the eye into the chamber between the lens and the retina, diffusing nutrients to the sensory cells.

THE VISUAL ACUITY OF BIRDS IS THOUGHT TO BE ABOUT THREE TIMES GREATER THAN THAT OF HUMANS. THE RABBIT IMAGES AT THE RIGHT ILLUSTRATE THIS DIFFERENCE, USING COMPUTER PIXELS TO REPRESENT THE NUMBER OF SENSORY CELLS IN THE EYE. BIRDS SEE A SHARPER IMAGE BECAUSE THEIR SENSORY CELLS ARE MORE ABUNDANT AND MORE DENSELY PACKED TOGETHER.

Elisabeth Rowan

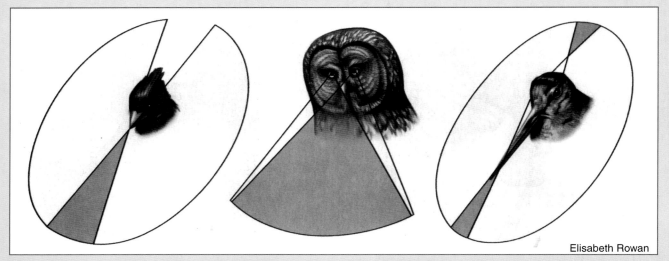

Elisabeth Rowan

MOST BIRDS, SUCH AS THE CARDINAL (LEFT), HAVE EYES POSITIONED ON THE SIDES OF THEIR HEADS, PROVIDING SUPERIOR PERIPHERAL VISION (LIGHT AREA) BUT A MUCH SMALLER FIELD OF BINOCULAR VISION (DARKER AREA IN FRONT). THE GREAT GRAY OWL (CENTER) HAS REDUCED PERIPHERAL VISION, BUT A MUCH GREATER FIELD OF BINOCULAR VISION. WITH ITS EYES SO FAR BACK ON THE HEAD, THE WOODCOCK (RIGHT) HAS BINOCULAR VISION BOTH FRONT AND BACK.

The eyes of most birds are located on the sides of the head, providing peripheral vision in excess of 340 degrees. While this great peripheral field has protective value for birds, it comes with a price tag. The lateral position of the eyes permits only a small area of binocular vision and, therefore, better depth perception. While this area of binocular vision is limited to less than 10 degrees in most birds, it is much larger in raptors—about 50 degrees in hawks and 70 degrees in owls. This gives raptors greater powers of depth perception. In some birds, such as cuckoos and woodcocks, the eyes are positioned far enough to the rear of the head to permit binocular vision both in front and behind the head, creating a superb defense mechanism. An unusual feature of bitterns permits both eyes to face forward in binocular fashion, even when the bill is pointed up in its familiar defensive posture.

Birds rarely blink (with the exception of owls, parrots, ostriches, and a few others) and close their eyes for sleeping by raising the lower lid. Usually unseen, however, is the third eyelid (nictitating membrane), located beneath the upper and lower lids, which moves horizontally across the eyeball. The movement of this eyelid across the eye resembles our blinking and serves to keep the eye moist. While humans lack this membrane, a remnant of it persists in the inner corner of our eye—a pink tissue called the nictitans. In some diving birds, the nictitating membrane has a transparent window that permits vision underwater while this membrane is closed.

Keenly adapted for low light conditions, with superior acuity and enhanced color capabilities and able to see in many directions simultaneously, the avian eye is an incredible structure. All they seem to be lacking is X-ray vision. Gee, I wonder....

A least bittern even with its bill pointed up in a defensive posture, still has forward-facing eyes for binocular vision.

Reprinted by permission of Kalmbach Publishing Co. from *Birder's World,* April 1998.

VISION AND THE BRAIN

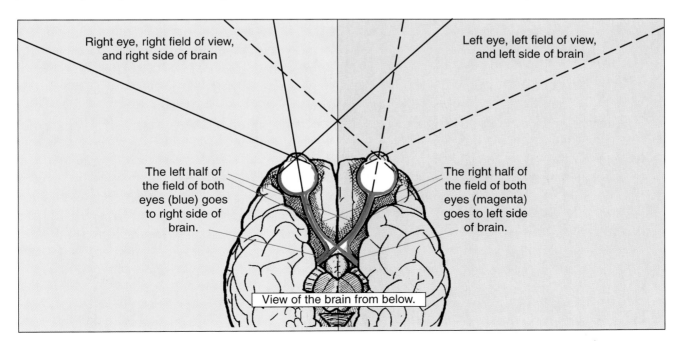

Vision is a complex interaction between light, the structures in the eye, and the brain. For you to see the words on this page, light must reflect off it and reach your eyes. That light hits your cornea, the curved outer surface of your eye, which does most of the focusing of the image. Next light enters the eye through the pupil, the adjustable opening in the iris. The image is focused by the lens, which lies just behind the iris, and by the vitreous humor, the jellylike sphere that fills the bulk of the eye. Finally, the image is projected on the retina, the delicate translucent tissue covering the back of the inside of the eye.

Once the optical system of the eye has projected an image on the retina, a complex series of electrochemical interactions begins that carries this image information to the brain. Light energy is transformed by the photoreceptors (rods and cones) into electric

messages, which travel to the optic disk, where the optic nerve connects to the eye. These thousands of messages, from each and every rod and cone, then travel via a thick nerve bundle called the **optic nerve.**

The optic nerves from both eyes extend through the fatty tissue at the back of the eye and into the skull. There the optic nerves from both eyes join at a point called the **optic chiasm,** where some nerve fibers from the left and right eyes cross over. Then they separate again into two nerve bundles.

As a result of this joining, information from the *left sides* of *both eyes* ends up going to the left side of the brain, and information from the *right sides* of *both eyes* goes to the right side of the brain. In this way, information about the visual field on the right side of the body goes to the left side of the brain, and vice versa.

Right eye, right field of view, and right side of brain

Left eye, left field of view, and left side of brain

The left half of the field of both eyes (blue) goes to right side of brain.

The right half of the field of both eyes (magenta) goes to left side of brain.

View of the brain from below.

After the optic chiasm the optic nerves continue back into the brain itself. The first stop for most messages is the **lateral geniculate nucleus (LGN)**, a structure inside the center part of the brain where initial processing of the visual image begins. At this point, input from the right visual field is still kept separate from that of the left visual field. This information passes to a thick group of long neurons called the **optic radiation.** The messages end up in the very back of the brain at the **visual cortex,** which processes input from both eyes to form a complete image. Right now you are seeing the words on the page!

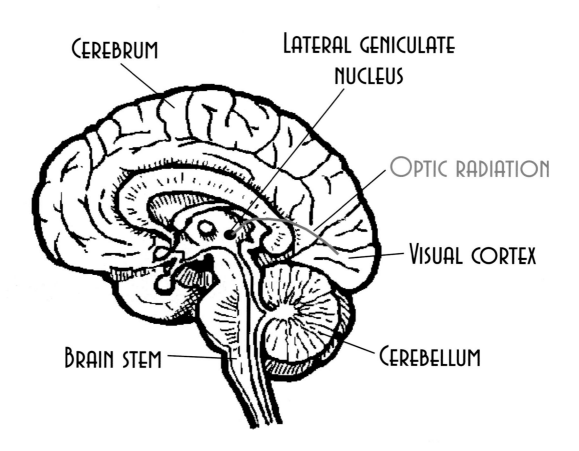

CEREBRUM

LATERAL GENICULATE NUCLEUS

OPTIC RADIATION

VISUAL CORTEX

CEREBELLUM

BRAIN STEM

Structures of the Human Brain

The human brain is a compact mass of tissue weighing about 1.5 kg (3 pounds). The brain and spinal cord make up the central nervous system, which is enclosed in bone. The brain is surrounded entirely by the cranium.

You can see three major parts of the brain without dissecting it, the **cerebrum,** the **cerebellum,** and the **brain stem.**

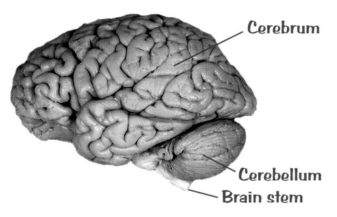

Cerebrum

Cerebellum

Brain stem

The most prominent part of the brain in humans is the large convoluted cerebrum. It has two halves or **hemispheres,** right and left, which look symmetrical and communicate with each other via a wide band of fibrous tissue known as the **corpus callosum.** The cerebrum makes up about 70% of the mass of the entire human nervous system.

The cerebrum has a distinctive set of convolutions or folds. The grooves in the surface of the cerebrum are called **sulci** (sul•see; singular **sulcus**) and the bumps are called **gyri** (JY•ree, singular **gyrus**). These form patterns that are similar for all humans, though individual variations exist.

The convolutions of the cerebrum enlarge the surface area of the cerebrum, called the **cerebral cortex.** The cerebral cortex integrates messages from the vast array of neurons to make sense out of the signals that come into the brain. Without this thin (about 3-mm thick) surface layer, we would be unable to process information, think logically, recognize faces, or plan ahead. The more folds a brain has, the more processing space it contains. The cerebrum of a rat, for instance, is smooth, implying that it does not do much processing of the information it receives. The brain of a dolphin, on the other hand, is more convoluted than a human's, suggesting a highly developed ability to make sense out of the world.

The cerebrum has regions, or **lobes,** that have specific functions. The **frontal lobe** coordinates much of what we think of as personality, including thinking and planning ahead, logical reasoning, emotional response, and the ability to concentrate. The **occipital lobe,** at the back of the cerebrum, processes visual information. The **parietal lobe,** located on the upper part of the side of the cerebrum, regulates the complex interaction between the brain and the body, coordinating incoming messages from touch and outgoing messages for movement. The **temporal lobe,** along the bottom of the side of the cerebrum, does more advanced processing of sensory input, and supports speech and language.

The small, densely striped structure that lies below and to the back of the brain is the **cerebellum** (little brain). It is also divided into two hemispheres. The cerebellum, which makes up about 11% of the mass of the brain, processes messages from muscles, tendons, and the inner ear, and uses this information to maintain balance and coordination.

In the center of the brain, in front of the cerebellum and below the cerebrum, is a relatively small, cordlike structure called the **brain stem.** It is an extension of the spinal cord and is the main pathway for messages to and from the rest of the brain. The brain stem regulates body functions such as heartbeat, breathing, and body temperature. You can survive damage to the cerebrum or cerebellum, but damage to the brain stem is usually fatal.

The brain stem also relays information from the body to the other parts of the brain. In general, the right hemisphere of the brain receives and sends messages to and from the left side of the body, and vice versa. So at some point in the pathway of nerves that connects the brain with a sensory system, there is an area of crossover where all of these nerves come together. That point is in the brain stem and is controlled by it.

Deep in the brain is a collection of structures known as the **limbic system.** The limbic system includes the **thalamus,** which helps relay sensory information to and from the cerebrum; the **hypothalamus,** which coordinates the regulation of body functions and controls the pituitary gland and its release of hormones; and the **amygdala,** which plays a role in emotions and memory.

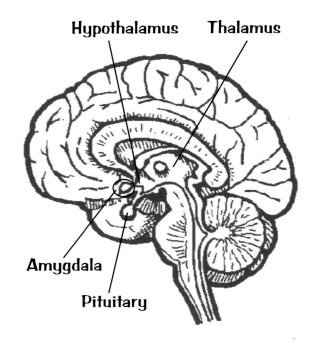

When you refer to the structures of the brain, several terms that describe orientation are useful. These anatomical terms apply to all living creatures and structures. The front is the **anterior;** the back is the **posterior.** The top is **dorsal,** and the bottom is the **ventral.** When a structure lies above another, it is **superior;** when it lies below another, it is **inferior.** These terms have nothing to do with value or status—just position.

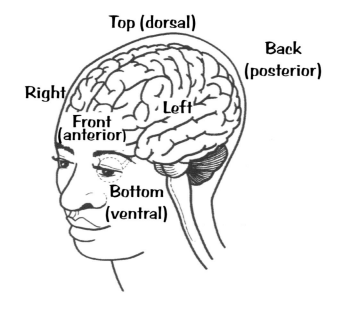

History of Brain Research

Every thought, emotion, action, and function of our bodies is controlled by the brain, a 1.5-kg organ that contains more than 60 billion individual parts that constantly communicate with each other during every moment of our lives. The human brain has been accurately referred to as the only organ that can study itself.

The study of the human brain is older than recorded history. Evidence suggests that the human brain has been in its present form since about 40,000 B.C.E. Some of our prehistoric ancestors even did a bit of brain surgery—there are human skulls from 10,000 years ago that have holes drilled in them, possibly to let out evil spirits that were thought to cause mental illness and headaches. In many cases these skulls show signs of healing, suggesting that the relief of pressure may have helped the patients live longer.

Hippocrates (circa 400 B.C.E.) was one of several ancient Greek scholars who thought that the brain is involved in sensing the environment. He suggested that the brain

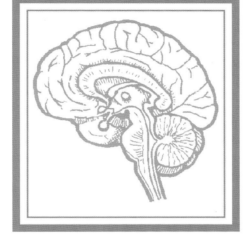

is also the seat of intelligence. The idea that the brain is the center of thought and consciousness was not accepted by all, including Aristotle (384–322 B.C.E.), who thought that the heart is the center of the intellect and that the brain's purpose is to cool the blood. This debate about the mind, or consciousness, and its relationship with the physical brain continues today, though most neuroscientists believe that emotional, psychological, and cognitive function could be understood and explained if enough were known about the biological and physical workings of the brain.

Careful observations of the structure and function of the brain were made by another Greek, Galen (circa 150 C.E.), who was the physician to the gladiators in Rome. He observed the effects of spinal-cord and head injuries, and carefully dissected animal brains. When he opened up the brain and found that it had hollow spaces filled with fluid, he suggested that this fluid was one of the so-called vital humors thought to be necessary for life. The brain was supposed to function by taking in and putting out this fluid to and from the body through the nerves, which were thought to be hollow tubes. This view was widely held for nearly 1500 years. In pictures of the body from this period, the ventricles are often drawn in exquisite detail, while the cerebrum is hastily sketched. The idea that the fluids are responsible for brain function was strengthened by the development of hydraulic pumps and mechanical devices. These devices seemed to model the idea that the brain sends out fluids to pump up the muscles to cause movement.

During the 1800s, our understanding of the brain and its function took great steps forward. Discoveries included the idea that nerves send electric messages that can be measured and timed; different areas of the brain have different functions; behavioral and physical traits can be inherited; and the neuron is the basic functional unit of the nervous system.

In the 1900s the study of the brain and nervous system exploded. In fact, the 1990s were designated the Decade of the Brain by the U.S. Congress. But there is still much to be learned. Neuroscientists study every possible level of organization within the brain. Some investigate the molecular level of brain function, including the chemicals that regulate the transmission of messages and formation of pathways and structures within the brain. Some study cells associated with the nervous system to learn how they operate on an individual level. Others analyze the system itself, to discover how all of the cells work together. Behavioral neuroscientists study the biological and physical basis for responses and reactions in the individual, and cognitive neuroscientists take up the age-old challenge of understanding the mechanisms that create consciousness.

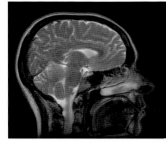

BRAIN-IMAGING TECHNIQUES

Different types of imaging devices are used to perform brain scans. The most common ones used for diagnosis are computerized axial tomography (CAT) and magnetic resonance imaging (MRI). Both CAT and MRI are used to study the structure of brain tissue. Electroencephalography (EEG) and positron emission tomography (PET) are used to study the activity levels in the brain. All of these techniques are noninvasive, which means that they do not require surgery to open the brain.

CAT

CAT combines an X-ray device and a computer. Before the CAT scan begins, the person being examined is injected with a contrast dye. The dye helps make any abnormal tissue more evident. The patient lies on a table that slides into a doughnut-shaped opening. While the patient lies very still, the CAT scanner circles the head, and X rays penetrate the brain. Absorption of X rays varies with the type of tissue penetrated. A ring of detectors measures the amount of X rays remaining after they pass through the brain. Thousands of thin cross-section readings feed into a computer, which transforms the data into a detailed picture.

MRI

The MRI is a tunnel-shaped piece of equipment. The person being examined lies on a table that slides into the tunnel. Inside the scanner, a magnetic field surrounds the patient's head while radio energy is beamed to the area. No X rays are used. The magnetic field changes the orientation of atoms in the brain. The radio waves cause another change of orientation. When the beam stops, the atoms relax and return to their original position. During relaxation, the atoms give off signals in differing amounts and at different intervals. Antennas pick up these signals and feed them into a computer, which assembles a picture. Because different atoms have their own characteristic radio signals, the computer can distinguish between healthy and diseased tissue.

MRI images are clearer than CAT images, but MRI imaging takes longer than CAT imaging, is more expensive, and is very noisy. Patients with cardiac monitors, pacemakers, or surgical clips cannot be imaged in an MRI because of the powerful magnetic fields.

EEG

In EEG several electrodes are attached to the patient's head and are usually held in place by a cap like a swim cap. The electrodes measure the electricity given off by the neurons in the brain as they send messages. The areas of highest activity give off the most electricity. The measurements for each electrode feed into a computer, which uses them to construct a detailed picture. Usually this picture is color-coded to show levels of activity, though it may just have shades of gray.

EEG scans only show activity on the surface of the cerebrum. They cannot show activity deep within the brain, unless an electrode is implanted surgically.

PET

In a PET scan a low-dose radioactive atom, produced by a cyclotron (an atom smasher), is attached to a chemical such as glucose (a sugar) and injected into the patient. The PET scanner rotates around the patient's head, detecting the rays emitted by the radioactive sugar. Measurements of brain activity (determined by concentrations of the glucose) feed into a computer, which produces a color-coded or shades-of-gray image of the brain as it converts glucose into energy. Highly malignant tumors consume glucose faster than normal brain tissue, so this method is effective at showing the location of tumors.

PET scans can show activity within the brain, as well as at the surface. The use of PET is limited because cyclotrons are scarce, so this technique is usually used in research and not for routine diagnosis.

DEPTH PERCEPTION

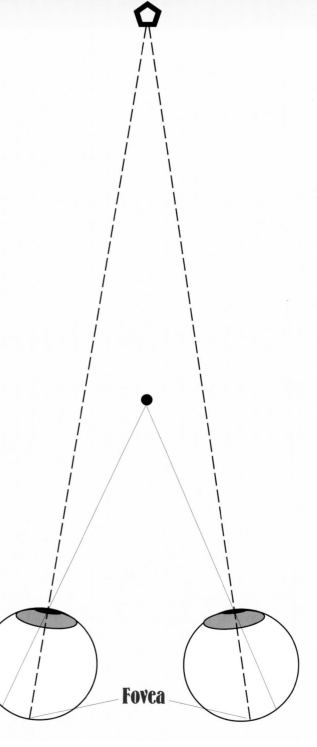

We take our three-dimensional world for granted, yet it is a complex task to convert the flattened image from our retinas into an image of depth. This ability, called **depth perception,** seems to be due to two major factors, both of which require two eyes, or **binocular vision.** The processes for determining depth and distance require prior experiences that help the brain learn.

One factor is the separation of your two eyes by about 7 cm. This separation means that the angle of viewing an object is slightly different for your right eye than for your left. Your brain takes the images that come to it from both eyes and processes these two slightly different images to calculate depth.

Another factor is convergence of the two eyes on the same point in space. As an object comes nearer, the eyes begin to cross as they both continue to focus on the object. The brain takes the information about the angle of each eye to calculate how far away an object is. The eye uses a kind of continuous triangulation system to get information about the position of objects distributed throughout space.

Fovea

When you focus on an object far away (see the dashed line on the illustration on page 50), both of your eyes look directly at it. The light from the object falls onto the fovea in both eyes. The brain puts the two images together to make one image because the images are in exactly the same location in both eyes.

Light from an object in the foreground (that you are *not* focused on) falls on two different regions of the retina, so the brain perceives two different objects in two different locations. As a result you see two images of the object in the foreground.

When you focus on an object close to you (see the dashed line on the illustration to the right), your eyes cross. The light from the object falls onto the fovea in both eyes. The brain puts the two images together to make one image because the images are in exactly the same location in both eyes.

Light from an object in the background (that you are *not* focused on) falls on two different regions of the retina, so the brain perceives two different objects in two different locations. As a result you see two images of the object in the background.

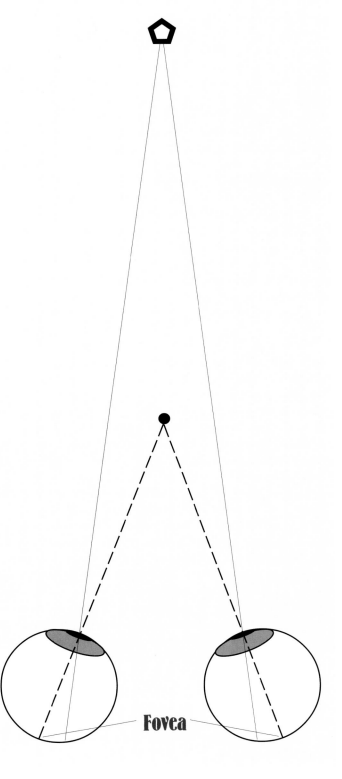

Fovea

OPTICAL ILLUSIONS

Perception seems to depend on experience. Therefore our early interactions with the world teach us how things usually look.

LIGHT

One type of optical illusion that stems from our early visual experiences of the world is based on shadows and light. When we see a curved surface that is lighter on the top than on the bottom, we perceive it as part of an object that juts out toward us. It looks as though light is falling on a curved object from a source above it, which is how we have experienced light in our natural environment. A similar figure that is lighter on the bottom than on the top is perceived as an indentation, since that is what an indentation would look like if the light were falling on it from above.

Test this illusion by turning the drawing below upside down. The circles that looked like indentations will look like bumps, and vice versa. The change in perception happens because of the change in your idea of the location of the light source—you assume the light is coming from the top of the page.

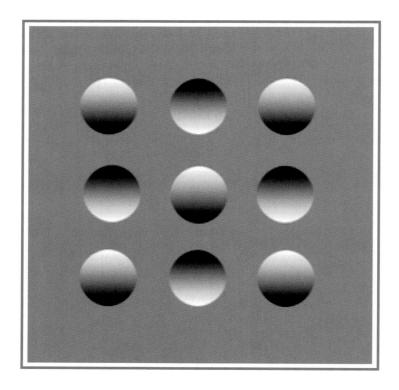

DISTANCE AND PERSPECTIVE

Several optical illusions are based on our experiences with distance. We learn at an early age that things that are far away look smaller than things that are close, even though we know that objects don't actually shrink as they go away from us. So if we see a picture that seems to show one object closer to us than another, we assume that the closer object is relatively smaller than the one that is far away. In the example below, the figure that seems closer to you looks much smaller, even though the two figures are identical.

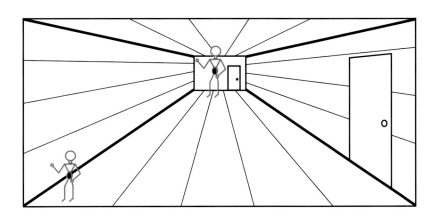

COMPARISON

Another type of illusion relies on comparisons that your brain makes when several lines or objects are next to each other. Our ability to judge angles and sizes is often distorted by the context of the objects. For example, in the figure below, the circle in the center on the left-hand side looks smaller than the one on the right, because it is surrounded by large circles that make it seem smaller.

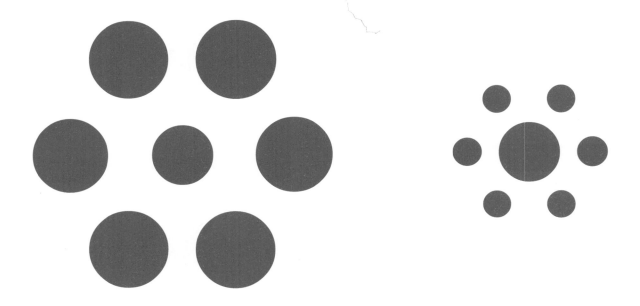

FILL IN THE MISSING DETAILS

Some illusions take advantage of the fact that your brain tends to look for patterns and fills in details, even if they aren't really there. For example, in the figure to the right, you see a triangle, even though there isn't really a triangle there at all. Your brain has seen triangles before, and it receives enough clues that it fills in the rest of the details.

FOREGROUND/BACKGROUND

Another type of illusion also takes advantage of your brain's attempts to find patterns or familiar shapes. The illusion to the right shows either two faces looking toward each other or a vase in the center, depending on which way you look at it. The brain can recognize both, because it has experiences with both. You cannot see both the vase and the faces at the same time, however; the images will pop in and out of view as you try to see them simultaneously.

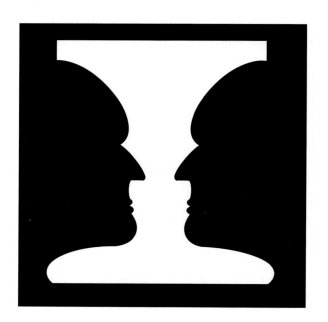

Sensory Perception

If a tree fell in a forest with nobody there to hear it, would it make a sound?

This age-old philosophical question has at its heart the issue of perception. Obviously, the tree falling would generate vibrations in the air around it, but the term *sound* implies the presence of a living being with the capacity to translate these vibrations into pitch and loudness. In the same way, vision is the capacity of a living being to translate the electromagnetic waves of certain frequencies into color, shape, and brightness. Color, tone, smell, taste, pain—these are all mental constructs that the brain builds from sensory stimulation of various kinds.

What we perceive depends on the range of physical stimuli that our sensory organs can gather and translate into information that travels to the brain. The human eye can perceive a narrow range of the electromagnetic spectrum. If we had the same capacity for vision as a honeybee, we would see in the range of ultraviolet light, and the world would look quite different. What would the world look like if we could see other frequencies such as microwaves, X rays, or infrared? What "color" would radio waves be? It is clear that our perception of the world leaves out much of reality.

One of the most complex abilities our brains have is recognizing faces. In a way that is not well understood, our brains can process information about the spatial features and patterns of a particular face, so that we recognize a person even if we see that person from a different angle. This ability develops quite early in infancy—even newborns seem to distinguish faces, and prefer faces to other shapes or figures. Yet, computer engineers have not been able to create this ability in artificial intelligence systems. The most sophisticated computer cannot do what a 1-year-old human can—recognize a face.

The brain can also receive a series of images, like a rapidly blinking light, and blend them to give the perception of constancy. We take this ability for granted, yet it is a complex task for the brain to blend images from the retina into a perception of a smooth, continuous whole. The brain does this constantly and seamlessly.

Makers of motion pictures have taken advantage of the brain's ability to create the perception of smooth motion from a series of individual images. Two processes seem to occur when we watch a movie.

First the brain holds onto and continues to "see" an image for a split second after it is no longer present. Early movies did not provide enough images or frames per second to allow the brain to fill in the gaps, so movement appears jerky and the scene seems to flicker.

Second the brain detects apparent movement from a series of individual images that move in relationship to each other. This process is not well understood, but in order for apparent motion to be realistic, objects in the images must move only a certain distance between images.

This apparent motion must match the brain's experience with actual motion.

Although we see the world as a whole, research suggests that at least three separate perceptual subsystems process visual information. One subsystem processes motion, one depth and form, and one color. Each subsystem follows the same basic pathway from the retina to the lateral geniculate nucleus to the cortex (surface) of the back of the cerebrum. The cerebrum seems to process these three classes of information separately and to blend them into a unified visual perception.

TOUCH RECEPTOR FIELDS

SENSE OF TOUCH

Next to vision, touch is arguably the most important sense we humans have for gathering information about the world around us. *Sense of touch* is a catchall phrase that includes four major types of sensation.

- Pressure (also sometimes called touch) is a mechanical stimulation of the skin.

- Pain (also called nocioception, from the Latin *nocere*, "to hurt") is sensed by separate receptors for sharp stabbing pain, for deep aches, and for damage caused by burning or freezing of skin.

- Temperature registers at separate receptors for hot and cold.

- Proprioception is the consciousness of the body moving and existing in space (including balance).

Each category of touch has its own receptors. A cross section of skin reveals several types of touch receptors.

The several types of pressure receptors include those that respond to fluttering and light touch, those that respond to deep steady indentation of the skin, and those that respond to vibrations. In addition, hair receptors wrap around the base of a hair follicle and signal any slight movement of the hair. Pain and temperature messages are sent by different types of bare nerve endings embedded in the skin.

Each of these receptors sends a message to the brain that tells it what type of touch that part of the skin has received. But how do all of these receptors work together to let the brain know how many different areas are being touched? For example, how do you know that someone is touching you with two fingers instead of just one? To answer that question, we need to learn more about how each receptor works.

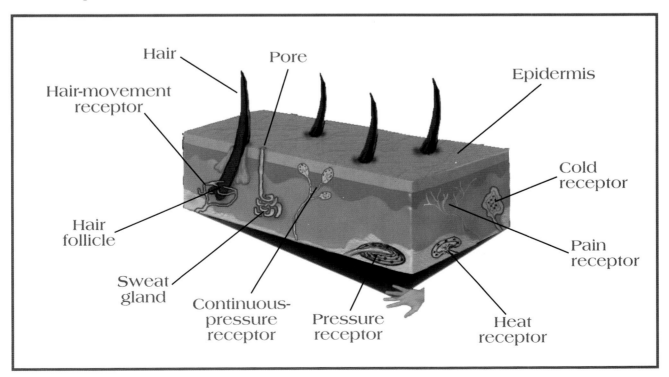

RECEPTOR FIELDS

Each sensory receptor has a receptive field, an area from which it gathers information. Each receptor can send only one message to the brain, no matter how many places in its receptive field are stimulated. The number, spacing, and size of the receptors determine two-point discrimination.

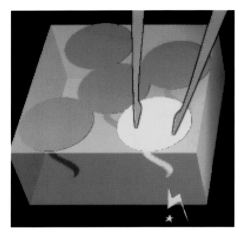

In this diagram you can see what would happen if the receptive fields for each touch receptor were large. When the two points of the tweezers touch the skin, both of them are inside the same receptive field, so that receptor sends a single message, even though two points touched the skin. The brain gets only one message, so it "feels" only one point. For the brain to "feel" two points, the skin must be touched in two different receptive fields, so that they both send messages to the brain.

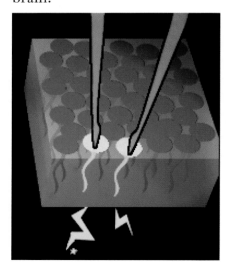

In this diagram you can see what would happen if the receptive fields for each touch receptor were small. When the two points of the tweezers touch the skin, each point is in a different receptive field, so both of the receptors send a message to the brain. The brain can "feel" two points, because two different receptors sent messages.

The number of receptors and the size of receptive fields vary in different areas of the body. If each receptor has a large receptive field, there are fewer receptors to cover the same area of skin. If each receptor has a small receptive field, more receptors fit in the same area of skin. The more receptors in a given area of skin, the smaller their receptive fields.

Our ability to discriminate between two points varies at least 20-fold in different areas of our bodies. Receptors for pressure are most densely packed in the fingertips and lips, and least densely spaced in areas of the back and legs. A good reason to read Braille with your fingertips rather than your elbow! The high density and small size of receptive fields in the fingertips allows an experienced Braille reader to discriminate between groups of up to six dots that are 1-mm high and spaced 2.5-mm apart, which make up one letter.

The high density and small receptive fields for touch in the lips also explain why babies put things into their mouths so often. They are not just tasting things—they are actually feeling them with their sensitive lips and mouths, gathering information with their sense of touch.

BRAIN MESSAGES

That Tickles!

An ant is walking on your arm. A tickling sensation attracts your attention, and you raise your other arm to brush the ant away. How does this happen?

Your touch receptors for the sensation we know as "tickle" were stimulated. They sent a message to your brain, alerting you to a problem. Your brain decided how to respond and sent messages to your arms, telling them how to move to brush away the ant.

Neurons at Work

The cells that make up your brain and all your nerves are called **neurons.** You have several hundreds of billions of neurons throughout your body and brain, which constantly send messages from one place to another.

Your touch receptors, photoreceptors (rods and cones), and receptors for hearing, taste, and smell are all on the ends of neurons called **sensory neurons.** Sensory neurons send information to the brain. The brain decides what to do about these messages. If your brain decides that you should move your arm, it sends out messages to the muscles in your arms, telling them to move. This job uses **motor neurons.**

Sensory neurons and motor neurons are both like wires carrying an electric signal. Sensory neurons carry messages to the brain, and motor neurons carry messages away from the brain. Sensory neurons give the brain information, and the motor neurons send instructions to the muscles. Your arm responds to the messages from the motor neurons by contracting certain muscles. Specialized sensory neurons, called stretch receptors, give the brain feedback, telling it how much the muscles are stretched or contracted. This communication between the brain, transmitted on the sensory and motor neurons, is happening constantly, not just in your arms, but all over your body.

Sending messages takes time. The longer the pathway, the longer it takes for a stimulus to produce a response. The interval is sometimes referred to as reaction time. You may have noticed this delay if you have ever stubbed your toe; you can see it being stubbed and hear the sound before you feel the pain! This delay occurs because the pathway from your eyes and ears to your brain is much shorter than the pathway from your toes to your brain. So the sensory neurons in your eyes and ears get their messages to the brain before the sensory neurons in your toes can.

NEUROTRANSMISSION:
Sending a Message

Inside your body lives an amazing and complicated communication system, even more complex than the most advanced computer or telecommunications network. Your brain and neurons are in constant action, sending and receiving billions of electric and chemical messages each day to keep everything, from the deep recesses of the brain to the remote wilderness of your toes, in touch. Let's take a closer look at this wonderful communication system.

Neurons

Neurons are the communication cells of the brain and nervous system, and they are specially suited to transmitting information from place to place throughout the body. Every neuron has three basic parts, which may look somewhat different, depending on where they are found in the nervous system.

The **cell body** is the operational center of the neuron, and contains the nucleus of the cell. Extending from the cell body are numerous branches called **dendrites** (*dendro* = tree), which receive incoming electric messages. The messages enter the dendrites, travel to the cell body, and depart from the cell body on another long, thin extension of the cell called the **axon.** At the end of the axon, the message passes to the dendrite(s) of one or more other neurons, and the message continues on its way.

The message is transmitted along the axon through electric impulses. This electric charge is not trivial; it is easily measured by electroencephalography (EEG). In fact, if you could connect neurons in just the right way, you could generate a substantial amount of electricity. This is how electric eels can generate a potential of several hundred volts.

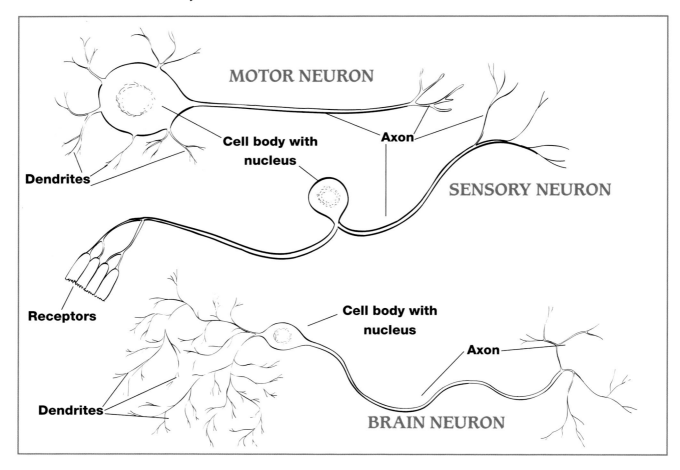

MOTOR NEURON

Cell body with nucleus

Axon

Dendrites

SENSORY NEURON

Receptors

Cell body with nucleus

Axon

Dendrites

BRAIN NEURON

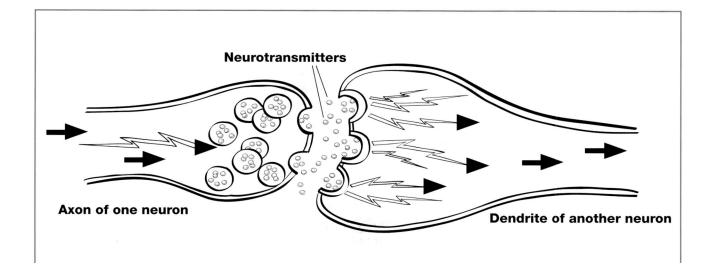

Neurotransmitters

Axon of one neuron

Dendrite of another neuron

Electric impulses are transmitted from one neuron to another with chemicals called neurotransmitters.

The Synapse: From Neuron to Neuron

Although neurons constantly carry information throughout the brain and body, and pass their messages from one to another, neurons do not touch each other. Instead, the axon of one neuron and the dendrite of the next are separated by a tiny gap called a **synapse.** Once an electric impulse reaches the end of an axon, it stimulates the release of chemicals called **neurotransmitters** into the gap in order to communicate with the next neuron in the pathway. These neurotransmitters fit into specific receptors on the surface of the receiving dendrite. When the chemical neurotransmitters trigger these receptors, they start an electric message in the receiving dendrite. The electric impulse races on down the axon and across the synapse to the next neuron, where the process repeats, perpetuating the message.

This combination of electric impulses (along the neuron) and chemical neurotransmitters (across the synapse) is why communication in the nervous system is called electrochemical.

Neurotransmitters: The Chemical Messengers

The several types of neurotransmitters are each involved in specific pathways of the brain. **Acetylcholine** (ACh) was the first neurotransmitter to be discovered. It transmits messages from motor neurons to muscle cells, as well as from neuron to neuron in many of the brain's pathways, especially those involved in learning and memory. **Dopamine** is thought to be involved in pathways that control movement and regulate emotional response. These pathways seem to be involved in schizophrenia and Parkinson's disease. **Norepinephrine,** also called **adrenaline,** is produced in response to stress or arousal. Patients with Alzheimer's disease seem to have deficiencies in this neurotransmitter. **Serotonin** seems to control mood, consciousness, depression, and anxiety. **Opioids,** such as **endorphins,** act much the same way opium or morphine does to reduce pain. These neurotransmitters cause the runner's high that many athletes report during elevated physical stress. Endorphins also appear to be released in the brain when a person eats chocolate, adding to the pleasure.

Neural Pathways:
The Communication Network

The typical human brain has 60 to 100 billion neurons, and each of these can make synaptic connections to hundreds, thousands, or even hundreds of thousands of other neurons. The huge number of pathways of neural activity that results is somehow responsible for everything a person learns, remembers, says, sees, and does—in fact, everything that makes a person human. These pathways are so important that brain development is one of the major growth spurts that babies experience, even before they are born.

Brain growth in the womb and in the first 5 years of life is rapid and extensive, compared to that of other systems within the body. The first budding of what will become the brain in a fetus occurs at 3 weeks, and by 5 weeks has clearly divided into the three main regions of the human brain. The developing brain has two major growth spurts. One takes place when the unborn baby is 15–20 weeks old, resulting in a huge number of neurons. The other begins at 25 weeks and continues until birth. The second growth spurt produces many **glial cells,** which support and nourish the neurons. A newborn's brain is already one-fourth of its adult size, and is much larger proportionally than the other parts of its body.

At birth a human has all of the neurons that he or she will ever have. In fact, babies lose a huge number of neurons before birth and in the first few years of life. What newborns and infants do not have is a well-developed system of communication *between* neurons. During the first few years of life, a baby's brain develops systems of interactions and communication among all of those neurons. Every time a baby looks at something, information enters its brain and forms a pathway between neurons. As the baby repeats the same or similar actions, that pathway gets stronger and those neurons thrive. Neurons that are not used do not become connected in strong pathways, and they eventually die. This redundancy in neurons gives the brain plenty of raw materials to use as it forms. Once the connections are made, the extra building materials are discarded.

Even though scientific breakthroughs are happening all the time, the story of neural pathways, and how they are formed and reinforced, is one of the biggest mysteries of brain research. Brain researchers have discovered that neurons grow more dendrites and make more synapses when they are stimulated by new learning. They have also shown that neurons actually grow closer together as these pathways are used and reinforced. Many mysteries remain, however, in our understanding of how neural pathways form, grow, and communicate.

SENSORY SYSTEMS

Awareness of the environment and the ability to respond quickly and decisively is absolutely essential for you to stay alive. Fortunately, you have been supplied with the early-warning systems needed to keep you fully informed of the potential hazards surrounding you. They are your senses and the central processor, your brain, that controls your every action.

STAYING ALIVE

Senses pick up clues from the environment, both far and near, and pass them on to the brain. The brain turns the clues over, compares them to previous experiences, and takes appropriate action.

All of our sensory systems have common characteristics. Each begins with one or several types of receptor cells that are specialized for receiving one class of environmental activity. In vision the stimulus is light of certain wavelengths that is converted into electric impulses by rods and cones in the retina. In the other senses the stimulus may be vibrations in the air that enter the ear, chemicals in a liquid on the tongue or gas in the nose, or mechanical pressure on the skin. In each of these cases, specialized receptor cells transform this environmental activity into an electrochemical signal that travels to the brain. In the brain the electric impulses are sorted out into our perceptions of vision, sound, taste, smell, and touch.

SENSORY INFORMATION

All sensory systems extract four basic types of information from stimuli.

1. **MODALITY** is the class of sensation, that is, vision, touch, taste, hearing, and smell. Each modality has several parts, or submodalities, such as color and movement in the visual system, and pressure, pain, cold, and hot in touch.

2. **INTENSITY** is the amount of sensation. For each sense, a threshold intensity of stimulus must be present for the system to detect anything. This threshold intensity may vary with training, fatigue, and the conditions under which the stimulus occurs. For example, a woman's pain threshold is usually elevated during childbirth, so that she can endure much higher levels of pain than normal.

3. **DURATION** is how long the perception of the sensation lasts. If the stimulus lasts a long time, the perceived intensity usually decreases, a

phenomenon known as adaptation. For example, when you first get into a hot bath, the temperature may feel unbearable, but this sensation fades quickly as heat receptors adapt to the stimulus.

4. **LOCATION** includes the ability to locate where the stimulation is taking place and the ability to distinguish two closely spaced stimuli. The latter is a function of the number and density of the receptors. The more densely packed the receptors, the closer two stimuli can act and still be detected by two separate receptors. For example, the fovea of the retina provides the greatest visual acuity, largely because of the high density of cone cells there.

Each sensory system has its own specific characteristics within this common pattern. Obviously, receptor cells in different sensory systems respond to different stimuli. In some cases receptors are specific for a certain submodality of a particular stimulus. An example of this is vision, where we find three types of cone cells, each of which responds to a different range of wavelengths of light. In other cases, such as hearing, the pattern of stimulation, that is, the frequency of the vibrations, distinguishes one sound from another.

Another way that sensory systems differ is in the area of the brain that processes messages from the receptors. In vision a large area at the back of the brain processes visual input. Touch involves an area along the top and center of the brain. For each sense the message to the brain takes essentially the same form—an electrochemical impulse. Where the brain receives the impulse determines whether we see or hear or smell something in response to the message.

Other animals have different ranges of sensory sensitivity than humans. Eagles see with greater acuity, bees see ultraviolet light, and rattlesnakes see infrared, or heat. Dogs hear higher sounds and whales lower sounds. Dogs can smell thousands of times better, and great horned owls don't smell at all. And some animals, particularly migratory waterfowl, seem to sense magnetism, although the exact mechanism and the organs are unknown.

Vision Overview

For vision the stimulus is light, which must be produced or reflected by an object. Light is a series of radiations of different wavelengths, which the visual sensory system sorts, processes, and perceives as different colors. Light is focused by the cornea and aqueous humor, passes through the pupil and into the eye, and is focused more by the lens and vitreous humor. The light then forms an image on the retina, which covers the back of the eye and contains the photoreceptors (rods and cones). Cones respond to color and detail and are concentrated in the center of the retina. Rods respond to dim light and are distributed more densely around the edges of the retina. Each photoreceptor sends an electric message to the optic nerve. The optic nerve sends the message to the center of the brain and then to the back of the cerebral cortex. Messages go from there to the frontal lobe and other areas of the cerebral cortex, where they are compared to previous experience so the observer can make sense out of what was seen.

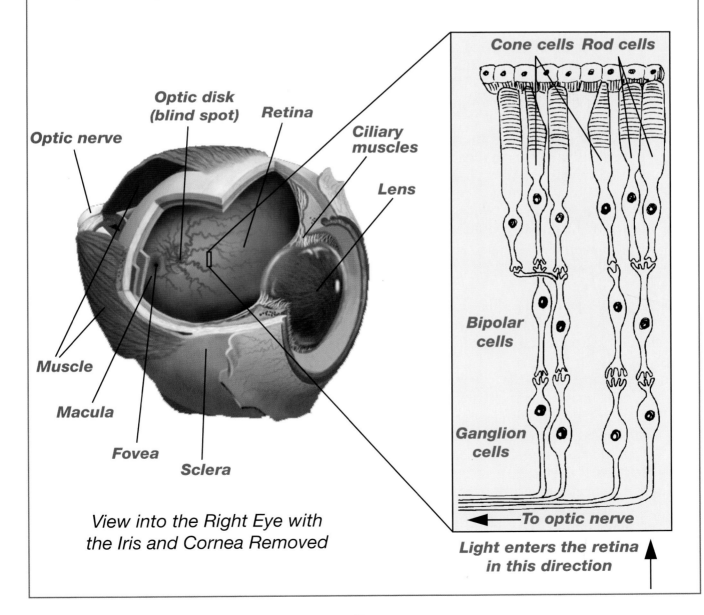

Optic disk
(blind spot)

Retina

Optic nerve

Ciliary
muscles

Lens

Muscle

Macula

Fovea

Sclera

*View into the Right Eye with
the Iris and Cornea Removed*

Cone cells Rod cells

Bipolar
cells

Ganglion
cells

To optic nerve

**Light enters the retina
in this direction**

Vision: Did You Know...?

✪ In the same way as you use one hand more than the other, you have one eye that you favor. To find out if you are right-eyed or left-eyed, make a circle with the thumb and index finger of one hand (the A-OK sign) and look through this circle at a small object across the room. Close one eye and then the other—the eye that sees the object inside the circle is your dominant eye.

✪ The iris gives the eye its color, depending on the amount of the pigment. All eye colors result from the same pigment, called melanin. This pigment also causes dark skin or freckles. Brown eyes have a lot of melanin; blue eyes have very little melanin.

✪ Your pupil may reveal more about you than you know. Studies have shown that, when people look at something they are interested in, their pupils expand or dilate. Shrewd merchants have used this fact for centuries, looking carefully into a potential customer's eyes to see if he or she is interested in what they are trying to sell.

✪ Color-vision problems affect about one in every 12 men and one in every 200 women. The most common difficulty is distinguishing between reds and greens, caused by a genetic defect in the red and green cones in the retina. Although this condition is often referred to as color blindness, true color blindness, or not seeing any color, is very rare.

✪ The eyes of insects are compound, made of hundreds or thousands of closely packed light-sensitive organs that gather light and focus it. The brain of an insect puts together all of these images to form a picture of the scene in front of it.

✪ An eagle has about five times more rods and cones in its retina than do humans, making its vision much more acute. In addition, its fovea, the area of greatest focus, is a deep pit, which helps to magnify the image even more. Eagles can spot prey the size of a rabbit 5 km (3 miles) away.

✪ As people get older, the lenses in their eyes become less flexible and less able to change shape to focus on objects that are close to them. For this reason they often hold things at arm's length to read or see details.

✪ Because the lens in the eye inverts light, the image on the retina is upside down. The brain flips the image back, so that you can see the world in the correct orientation. Scientists have done experiments with people wearing special glasses that invert the image so that the world looks upside down. After wearing these for a few days, the brain compensates for the inverted image, and the person can see the world as right side up again. When they remove the glasses, the world once again looks upside down for a few days before the brain recompensates to return to normal vision.

✪ Alcohol and tobacco use can damage the optic nerves in some people. Excessive alcohol consumption also can cause blurred vision or double vision. Alcohol interferes with the way the eyes work together and how the signals travel to the brain.

Touch Overview

For touch the stimulus can be an array of mechanical or thermal signals, such as pressure, pain, cold, hot, and continuous pressure. The skin, which covers the entire body, contains sweat glands, hair, and touch receptors. Different receptors respond to pressure, pain, cold, heat, and continuous touch. Each receptor sends an electric message to a sensory neuron. The sensory neurons send the message into the spinal cord, through the center of the brain, and to the top of the cerebral cortex.

Messages go from there to the frontal lobe and other areas of the cerebral cortex, where they are compared to previous experience so the observer can make sense out of what was touched.

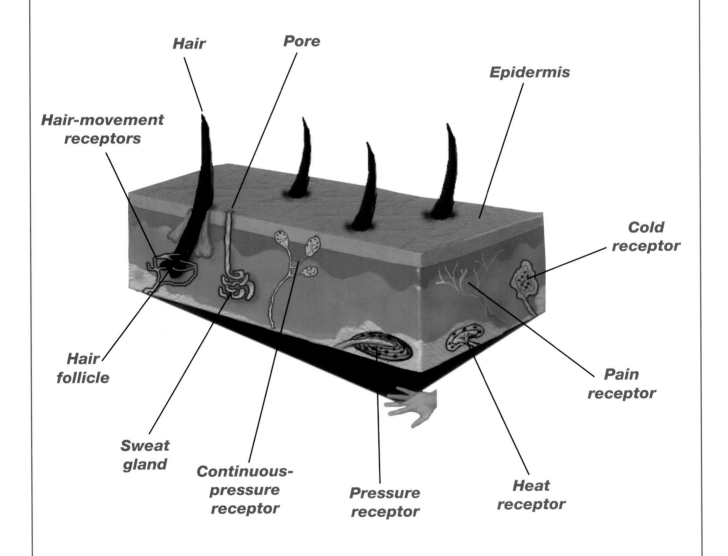

67

Touch: Did You Know...?

✪ In the disease of leprosy, pain receptors are damaged and do not send pain messages when parts of the body are hurt. People with leprosy do not know when they are harming their own bodies, because pain messages don't warn them. This lack of awareness causes a lot of damage, especially to extremities such as hands and feet. As a result, parts of the body that are damaged become infected and inflamed, and eventually can even decay.

✪ Skin is the body's largest organ, covering the entire surface of the body. In addition to containing millions of touch receptors, it protects against infection, injury, and harmful radiation from the Sun, and helps control body temperature. Your skin weighs 3–4.5 kg (6–10 pounds) and would cover an area of 152 m (356 feet) if it were spread out flat.

✪ Scientists don't really understand what makes people ticklish, but it seems to come from very small nerve endings just under the surface of the skin. The response to being tickled is involuntary, usually involving laughter, a sense of alertness, and increased pulse rate and blood pressure.

✪ Goose bumps are the result of messages sent to the brain by cold receptors in the skin. The brain sends a message to the blood vessels and muscles in the skin, causing small bumps to form that help reduce the loss of body heat.

✪ Being touched is important for normal development. If babies are not cuddled and held a lot, they don't grow fast, have difficulty learning, don't form emotional attachments to people, and may even die.

✪ Itching is caused by an irritation to the skin from things such as infections, allergies, insects, or fabrics. The irritation moves small touch receptors in the skin, which produces an itching sensation. If you scratch that area you may relieve the irritation, or it may cause pain receptors to fire, which neutralizes the itching.

✪ Another part of our sense of touch is the sense of balance. Keeping our balance is a complex interaction between several types of touch receptors, including sensory input from muscles and organs throughout the body, information from the inner ear, and signals from pressure against surfaces such as the ground or floor.

✪ Many sensations result from a combination of receptors sending messages to the brain. For example, no touch receptors sense wetness. Instead, the brain receives messages from cold receptors and from pressure receptors, which it combines to give the message that the skin is wet.

✪ When you have a sharp pain in a small area, such as a pin prick, it helps to rub the area. Rubbing activates pressure receptors in the skin, and decreases the intensity of the pain receptors' message to the brain.

Hearing Overview

For hearing the stimulus is sound, which must travel through gas, liquid, or solid to reach the ear. Sound is a series of vibrations of different wavelengths, which sound like different pitches. Sound waves are gathered and focused by the outer ear, and then they strike the eardrum and start it vibrating. Vibrations pass along the three tiny bones in the middle ear (the hammer, anvil, and stirrup) to the inner ear, or cochlea, which is a snail-shell-shaped coil that contains fluid and hair cells. Hair cells in the cochlea bend slightly in response to vibrations, sending electrical messages to the auditory nerve. Each hair cell responds to a particular wavelength of vibration. The auditory nerve sends messages through the center of the brain to the side, the temporal lobe of the cerebral cortex. Messages go from there to the frontal lobe and other areas of the cerebral cortex, where they are compared to previous experience so the observer can make sense out of what was heard.

Cross Section of the Cochlea

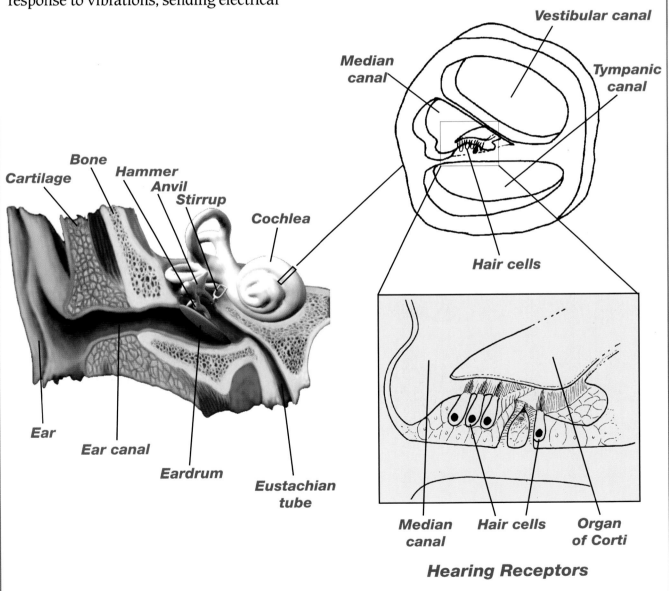

Vestibular canal

Median canal

Tympanic canal

Bone

Cartilage

Hammer
Anvil
Stirrup

Cochlea

Ear

Ear canal

Eardrum

Eustachian tube

Hair cells

Median canal   Hair cells   Organ of Corti

Hearing Receptors

Hearing: Did You Know...?

✪ When you hear your own voice on tape, it probably doesn't sound the way you expect it to. When you hear your own voice as you talk, the sound travels through your jawbone and mouth as well as through the air in your ear. When you hear your voice on tape, the sound is traveling only through air, so it sounds different.

✪ When you "hear the ocean" in a large seashell, what you are actually hearing is your own pulse. The smooth spiral shape of the shell amplifies the smallest of sounds into the kind of roar we associate with the ocean.

✪ The earliest hearing aids were large horns or cones that a person pointed toward the source of sound they wanted to hear. Electronic hearing aids are much more effective, because they can amplify sounds. Scientists are experimenting with hearing aids that are surgically implanted inside the ear.

✪ Ludwig van Beethoven, the famous composer, first noticed that he was having trouble hearing when he was about 30 years old. By the time he wrote some of his most famous symphonies, he was almost completely deaf and couldn't hear performances of his compositions. Scientists think that Beethoven had the type of deafness known as otosclerosis, which can be treated easily today.

✪ Sound volume is measured in decibels. A sound that is just barely audible is about 10 decibels, while a jet airplane taking off is about 150 decibels. Every increase of 10 decibels represents ten times as much sound. This means that a 20-decibel sound is not twice as loud, but ten times as loud as a 10-decibel sound.

✪ Rock music can produce sounds of 120–130 decibels on a stereo, and is even louder at concerts. Long exposures to sound levels above 80 decibels can permanently damage hair cells in the ear, particularly those that receive higher frequency sounds.

✪ By the age of 40, most Americans have lost some hearing, especially in higher frequency ranges. This appears to be a result of living in an industrial nation, because people in small villages in nonindustrial countries do not show this hearing loss with age.

✪ Excessive noise has been shown to cause higher blood pressure, faster heartbeats, emotional distress, learning difficulties, disturbed sleep patterns, and susceptibility to accidents. In addition, high noise levels make workers less productive.

✪ Most people can hear sounds of frequencies ranging from 16 to 20,000 cycles per second. This represents about ten octaves. Many animals, such as dogs and cats, can hear much higher frequencies. Cats use this ability to locate their food—mice make high-pitched sounds that cats can hear, which helps them locate and catch the mice.

✪ Having two ears helps you locate sounds. Sounds enter both ears, and the brain uses differences in loudness and arrival time at the receptors to locate the source of the sound.

Taste Overview

For taste the stimulus is a series of chemicals that are dissolved in liquid on the tongue. Chemicals dissolve in the saliva and touch the tongue, which has taste buds along the edges of the bumps that cover it. The sides of the taste buds have receptors that respond to only one type of basic taste chemical, either salt, sweet, sour, or bitter. When that type of chemical touches the receptor, it sends an electric message to a neuron. The taste bud neurons send messages through the center of the brain to the cerebral cortex of the temporal lobe. Messages go from there to the frontal lobe and other areas of the cerebral cortex, where they are compared to previous experience so the observer can make sense out of what was tasted.

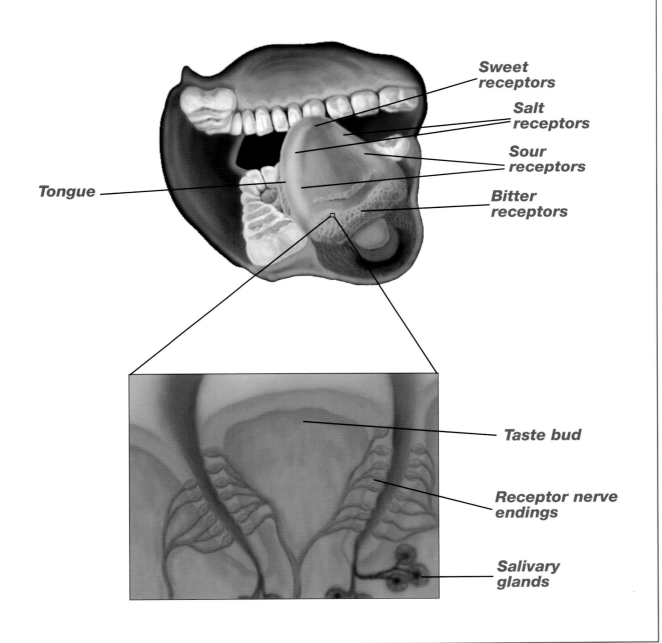

Sweet receptors

Salt receptors

Sour receptors

Bitter receptors

Tongue

Taste bud

Receptor nerve endings

Salivary glands

Taste: Did You Know...?

○ Babies have many more taste buds than adults, and their taste buds are all over the inside of their mouths, rather than concentrated on the tongue as in adults. As a result babies and young children are often picky about what they eat, and they may prefer bland foods. As people get older, their sense of taste becomes less sensitive, so they can enjoy more flavorful or spicier foods than younger people.

○ Taste buds last about 10 days before new ones replace them. A new taste bud can grow in 12 hours.

○ In humans, taste and smell are related. Taste buds distinguish between four basic types of taste—salt, sour, sweet, and bitter. The rest of the "tastes" we distinguish are actually smells. So when you have a head cold or other condition that stuffs your nose with mucus, you lose much of your sense of taste.

○ Chili peppers cause pain receptors in the tongue and mouth to send messages to the brain. The messages stimulate the brain to release endorphins, the natural painkillers of the brain. The endorphins produce feelings of pleasure, and possibly enhance other flavors in the food.

○ The tongue produces saliva, which helps break down food to start the digestive process. Chemicals in food dissolve in saliva, making them accessible to the receptors in the taste buds.

○ Taste buds that detect sweet tastes are on the front of the tongue for many animals. Because most naturally sweet plants are good to eat, the tip of the tongue can be used to do a quick survey of what an animal should eat.

○ Bitter receptors are usually in taste buds on the back of the tongue. Because most things that are naturally poisonous are also bitter, the rows of bitter taste buds help to detect food that could be dangerous before it is swallowed. When the bitter taste buds are activated, a gag reflex causes the animal to cough up the food. In this way, the taste buds help protect the animal from eating something harmful.

○ One out of every 20 people who has a head injury experiences a loss of taste and/or smell.

Smell Overview

For smell the stimulus is a wide array of chemicals that evaporate in the air and dissolve in the mucus of the nose. The seven basic odor types are floral, mint, camphor, ethereal, musk, pungent, and putrid. Chemicals in the air are drawn into the nasal cavity and up to the olfactory surface, which is in the top of the nose, and is covered with mucus to dissolve the chemicals. The olfactory surface has several types of receptors, each of which responds to one or a combination of the basic odor types. The chemical molecule fits into a special shape on the receptor that sends an electric message to a neuron. The olfactory neurons send a message to the olfactory bulb, a structure under the frontal lobe of the cerebrum, then to the temporal lobe of the cerebral cortex. Messages go from there to the frontal lobe and other areas of the cerebral cortex, where they are compared to previous experience so the observer can make sense out of what was smelled.

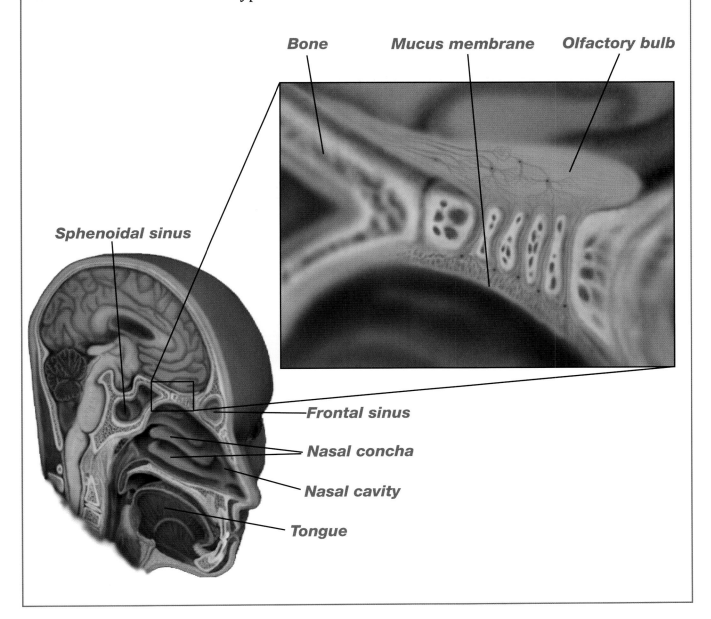

Bone

Mucus membrane

Olfactory bulb

Sphenoidal sinus

Frontal sinus

Nasal concha

Nasal cavity

Tongue

Smell: Did You Know...?

✪ Even though humans do not rely on their sense of smell to the same extent as other animals, the average person can distinguish about 4000 distinct odors. Extremely sensitive people can distinguish about 10,000 different smells. Women tend to have a more acute sense of smell than men.

✪ Many insects have a very acute sense of smell. A male silkworm can identify a female silkworm from more than 3 km (2 miles) away.

✪ Your sense of smell is about 10,000 times more sensitive than your sense of taste. Scientists have discovered that even a single molecule of a particular chemical in the air can trigger a smell response.

✪ Your sinuses are basically holes in your head that are filled with air. Each sinus has a lining that produces mucus that drains into the nose and throat. When this layer gets infected or inflamed, mucus cannot drain and builds up, causing pressure and pain.

✪ Hay fever is not a fever at all, but an allergic reaction to pollen, dust, mites, or other small particles in the air. These particles cause the mucus layers in the nose to become inflamed and irritated, making them swell up, itch, and produce a runny nose.

✪ Odors are very powerful memory triggers. About 85% of people have some sort of childhood memory that is linked to a particular smell, the most common of which is baking bread. Memories triggered by odors are often emotionally intense and vivid, more so than in other senses.

✪ If you want to identify a smell more accurately, take a deep breath. Air will swirl around inside your nasal cavity and come into contact with many different olfactory receptors, increasing the chances that the correct receptors will fire.

✪ Just as you use one hand more than the other, you have a dominant nostril. If you are right-handed, your right nostril will be more sensitive to smells than your left nostril.

✪ The sense of smell is the least understood of our senses.

✪ Smoking can seriously impair your sense of smell and can cause long-term damage to your olfactory system.

BRAIN MAPPING

Scientists have learned quite a bit about which parts of the brain are responsible for different functions, through a variety of methods. Information from several studies has contributed to a sort of map of the brain, showing which areas are responsible for which activities.

The earliest studies involved people who had brain damage that was not caused by scientists or doctors. For example, one of the most famous studies in neuroscience was the story of Phineas Gage, a foreman at a railroad construction site in 1848. While preparing to blast a hole in the rocks, he had an accident. An iron rod shot into his head just below his eye, went through the front part of his brain, and left at the top of his skull.

Amazingly enough, Gage did not die, but recovered after a doctor cleaned out the wound as well as he could. Throughout the rest of his life, however, his personality was different. Before the accident, he had been a hard-working, intelligent, polite man. Afterward, he acted like a spoiled child, always wanting his own way, not caring how his actions affected other people, and restlessly starting one project after another, but never finishing anything. He was stubborn, impatient, and mean. Because he was so unpleasant, most of his friends and family felt he wasn't Phineas anymore.

The case of Phineas Gage gave doctors evidence that many characteristics of a person's personality seem to be located in the front region or lobe of the brain. By the mid-1900s this discovery, along with other studies, led to the use of an operation called the frontal lobotomy. This brain surgery involved removing or damaging a large part of the frontal lobe. Surgeons performed lobotomies on people with violent tendencies, to change their personality and to make them calmer.

Although this operation had positive results with some patients, the side effects were drastic and involved the same sorts of changes as in Gage's case. These included an inability to plan and concentrate, and a deadening of the emotions. This operation was performed a lot right after World War II, but because of the side effects it is used very rarely today.

Head wounds were particularly common in World War II because of the types of weapons used. Following the war doctors and scientists observed soldiers to discover what they could about the specific role of different parts of the brain. For example, if a certain part of the brain was damaged and the person could no longer hear or see, scientists inferred that the part of the brain that was damaged had something to do with hearing and vision. This sort of study is difficult, however, because scientists cannot plan how they would like to study the structure/functions relationship in the brain. Because scientists would never purposefully destroy or damage a person's brain, they could study only the injuries that happened by accident.

Because of the difficulties in studying human brains, scientists began using animals in more detailed and controlled studies of brain function. Much of what we know about the location and function of memory, learning, and our senses comes from brain research on animals. In some studies, rats were taught to do a task such as running a maze. Then certain tiny parts of their brains were removed. After the operation, they were put into the maze again. If they could not remember how to run the maze, scientists had evidence that they had located an area of the brain that is used for memory.

Some of what we know about the location of different brain functions is from studies of patients with a disease called epilepsy. This condition is caused by sudden, brief changes in electric activity. Neurons send their signals much more quickly than normally, causing a sort of electric storm in the brain known as a seizure. A pattern of repeated seizures is epilepsy. Head injuries, brain tumors, lead poisoning, problems in the brain's development before birth, and certain inherited and infectious diseases can all cause epilepsy, though in about half of all cases the cause is unclear.

In the most common type of epilepsy, the seizures start with a burst of activity in the left hemisphere of the brain, in an area known as the temporal lobe. In the 1930s, doctors began to do operations on these epilepsy patients in order to stop the spread of the seizures. They thought that if they could remove the part of the brain that started the seizures, the patients would not have any more seizures.

In this type of brain surgery, the patient is awake. Because there are no pain or touch receptors inside the brain itself, only the patient's skin is numbed while the surgeons open the head to see the brain. During the surgery, before removing any brain tissue, the doctors send small electric signals to specific points on the brain to see what that part of the brain does. The doctors want to be sure that they do not remove a part of the brain that the patient needs for moving or feeling, so they find those areas by probing with their signals.

For example, a doctor would send a signal by touching a small part of the brain. The patient may move a finger or toe, showing that the brain uses that area for movement. Or the patient may say it tickles or feels like something is crawling up an arm or leg. The doctors know that this area is responsible for touch messages. Results from these operations have been very helpful for mapping the brain.

Some methods for mapping the brain do not involve injury to or surgery on the brain. These techniques are noninvasive: they don't require a physical change in the brain's structure. Noninvasive techniques for studying brain activity include the electroencephalogram, or EEG, which measures the electric activity in the brain, and positron emission tomography, or PET, which measures the brain's use of energy. Both of these methods have been very useful for scientists studying the location of specific functions in the brain. Using all of the results of these types of studies, scientists have constructed a general map of brain functions.

The General Map

Messages about touch are processed by an area of the cerebral cortex, or surface of the cerebrum, on the middle and top of the brain, extending down the sides. The area for movement is directly next to the area for touch, so that information from touch signals can be sent easily and quickly to the areas responsible for movement.

In vision, the optic nerve sends messages to the center of the brain and then to the back part of the cerebral cortex, which processes the image and puts it back together.

In hearing, the auditory nerve sends messages through the center of the brain to the side of the brain, the cerebral cortex of the temporal lobe.

The taste-bud neurons send messages through the center of the brain to the cerebral cortex of the temporal lobe.

The olfactory neurons send a message to the olfactory bulb, a structure under the frontal lobe of the cerebrum, then to the cerebral cortex of the temporal lobe. Because messages go directly into the center of the brain, the part that seems to respond to emotions and learning, smells can bring back very strong and emotional memories, unlike other senses.

In all senses, messages eventually go to the frontal lobe and other areas of the cerebral cortex. There they are analyzed and compared to previous experiences in order to understand and evaluate what the person has sensed.

How much brainpower is used for different functions?

In these general sensory areas are specific locations and regions that are responsible for aspects of our senses. For example, although messages from touch receptors all go into the same general area of the brain (purple area below), each part of the body sends messages to specific locations within the general "touch" area.

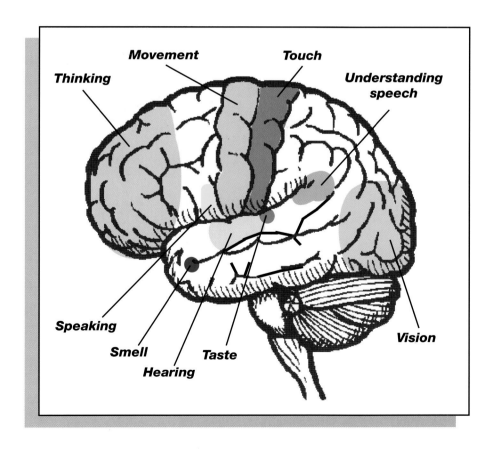

Figure A below shows which part of the surface of the brain receives touch information from each area of the body.

The exaggerated parts of the body in the drawing, such as the hand and fingers, lips, and tongue, are laid next to the areas of the brain that receive information from them. Large areas of the brain are dedicated to touch information from these parts because more receptors in these parts are sending messages that must be interpreted.

Another way scientists represent the number of receptors in different parts of the body is shown below in Figure B. This type of a drawing is called a homunculus, meaning "little person." This representation also exaggerates different parts of the body to show how sensitive they are. Can you see which parts of the human body are best equipped to gather information through the sense of touch, and which parts are poorly equipped?

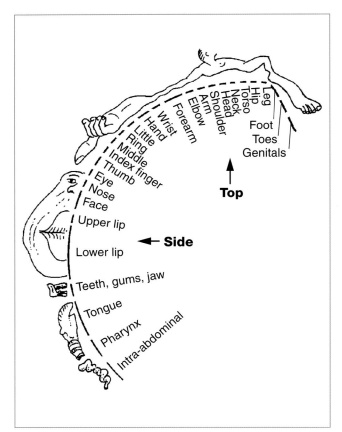

Figure A. Coronal Section of the Brain through the Touch Region.

Figure B. Exaggerated representation of the human body drawn according to how sensitive each area is.

How Can Our Senses Fail Us?

Each of our senses involves a highly complex series of interactions between several parts of the body, including the specialized organ to gather the stimulus, receptors that translate the stimulus into electricity, the neurons that carry the messages to the brain, and the brain itself, which processes these messages into a perception of the world around us. There are several ways that a sense can fail to function correctly; in fact, it is somewhat amazing that any of our senses do function correctly!

Something may go wrong with the organ that receives the stimulus. For example, in vision, the lens or cornea of the eye may not focus or transmit light correctly. With cataracts the lens darkens and reduces the amount of light getting into the eye. With astigmatism the cornea is not perfectly curved, and this results in an area of blurriness in a person's vision. In the case of nearsightedness or farsightedness, the lens does not focus the image on the retina, but instead focuses slightly in front of or behind the retina.

Conditions affecting the organ that receives the stimulus may be permanent or temporary. For example, when you have a cold, mucus builds up inside your nose, interfering with your sense of smell, but once the cold goes away, your sense of smell returns to normal. Conditions can also be age-related. Most people experience a certain amount of hearing loss with age.

Something may go wrong with the receptor itself. A receptor might not respond correctly (or at all) to the stimulus. When you bite into a piece of pizza hot from the oven and burn your tongue, your taste buds are damaged, but they will be replaced by new ones within a few days. Other conditions may be more permanent, such as damage to the hair cells (hearing receptors) caused by exposure to extremely loud sounds at an overamplified rock concert. In the disease of leprosy, pain receptors in the skin are damaged so that the person cannot feel pain.

In some cases the receptors may be missing completely. A significant number of people (mostly males) are missing the cone cells that respond to certain colors of light. This results in color blindness, a condition that is more inconvenient than dangerous.

Something may go wrong with the connection between the receptor and the brain. In cases of retinal detachment, the cones and rods function just fine, but the message cannot get to the brain because the neurons are disconnected— unplugged. When the spinal cord is cut or damaged, messages cannot go into or out of the brain, so the person is paralyzed and cannot feel anything.

Something may damage the brain. Head traumas from cycling and sports accidents or other head blows, as well as brain diseases, including tumors, can affect the part of the brain responsible for processing sensory information. An infant's sensory mechanism may not develop completely, so that the brain never learns how to process sensory information correctly. For example, when children have crossed eyes, it is important to correct the condition as early as possible because the eyes need to "train" the brain how they work together. If this development does not occur at the correct time, the eyes may function perfectly well, but the brain will not process the information correctly.

Your Mind Can Map Your Destiny

By Ben Carson

Dr. Ben Carson, 52, is the director of pediatric neurosurgery at Johns Hopkins Children's Center, a position he has held since 1984. He first received worldwide fame in 1987, as the principal surgeon in the 22-hour separation of the Binder Siamese twins from Germany—the first time that twins connected at the back of the head had been separated with both infants surviving.

Dr. Carson grew up in poverty in Detroit and Boston. He started out with terrible grades, anger, and low self-esteem. But once he made a decision to change his life by harnessing the power of his mind, nothing could stand in his way.

It was the sharpest knife I had ever seen. The anatomy instructor wielded the instrument with a skill that only years of experience could convey as he exposed the glistening white skull of an elderly female cadaveric donor. Using an air-powered drill, he created a series of holes in the skull, then made connecting cuts with a power saw. Bone dust and a strange odor filled the air. Then, without fanfare, he pried loose a large segment of skull and lifted it off. The anticipation was intense. This would be my first glimpse of the human brain.

Moments before, my mind had briefly escaped the formaldehyde-laden air as I wondered: "Who is this lady who so generously made her body available to teach the next generation of physicians? What motivated her? What connection did the brain I was about to explore have to her dreams, the life she had made for herself?" As I delved into the secrets of the brain, such questions would continue to fascinate me.

I was somewhat disappointed as the bony lid was elevated, revealing a smooth, grayish surface crisscrossed by numerous blood vessels. The instructor quickly informed the four first-year medical students gathered at the dissection table that they were looking at the dura mater (Latin for "tough mother"), a protective, leatherlike covering of the brain and spinal cord. He made a nick in the dura with a scalpel, extended it into a large semicircle, and folded it back.

It was like opening the cover of a treasured manuscript that had been found after a long search. There it was—the most beautiful and impressive object I had ever seen! I felt an immediate connection with the grayish-pink nebulous mass, which looked like the sleeping quarters of a bevy of obese worms overlaid by a delicate spiderweb that had ensnared various-sized strands of colored thread.

The intricate strands of my own mind had led me here. Despite dire poverty, I had decided at age 8 that I wanted to be a doctor. In college, I majored in psychology and took courses that explored the psychological and functional aspects of the brain.

Dr. Ben Carson with 4-year-old Alex Cockey, a hydrocephalic patient, during a follow-up visit at Johns Hopkins Children's Center with his parents, Catherine and Alexander Cockey.

At medical school, I decided to make neurosurgery my lifelong passion. I was impressed by the clinical presentations made by the neurosurgeons there, but the deciding factor was my own analysis of my God-given gifts: I had a tremendous amount of eye-hand coordination as well as an ability to think and visualize in three dimensions, a crucial skill. The brain does not contain many landmarks, and a neurosurgeon must be able to imagine readily where all the numerous nuclei, tracts, and neurological pathways are situated.

After that first glimpse around the dissection table, the landscape of the brain continued to hold a fascination for me. Two years later, I saw it again in a living patient. Once again, I awaited the moment of revelation. This time, as the dura was folded back, the mysterious mass pulsated with

life—and I had a sudden, startling insight: This conglomerate of billions of neurons and hundreds of billions of interconnections was the actual physical thing that gave each of us our distinct personality, the intellectual and emotional characteristics that made each person unique.

The organ system of the brain is one of incredible complexity and power. It can process millions of pieces of information per second. It remembers everything a person has ever seen or heard. For example, by placing special electrodes into the parts of the brain that control memory, you can stimulate recall in an 85-year-old so specific that he could quote verbatim a newspaper article read a half century earlier.

One characteristic of the brain in particular makes us essentially human and distinguishes our brains from those of other animals: the presence of very large frontal lobes. They enable us to engage in rational thought-processing, to extract information from the past and the present, analyze it, and use our conclusions to project a course of future action.

Other animals are victims of circumstance. They can only react to their environment. But humans, thanks to our frontal lobes, can plan, strategize, and exercise control over our environments. We don't have to be victims who simply react.

I learned that truth about frontal lobes at age 10, when—not doing well in school and guided initially by my mother's firm hand—I made a decision to change my life's direction. Within a year and a half, by devouring book after book, I had migrated from the bottom of my fifth-grade class to the top of my seventh-grade class. This academic transformation was so dramatic that one might have suspected a brain transplant, if such a thing were possible. The actual change occurred in my self-perception and my expectations. I had gone from victim to master planner.

frontal lobes

Lateral and ventral views of the brain illustrating a human's pronounced frontal lobes.

By the age of 14, my mind was plotting my future. Reading the biographies of successful people, I realized that I could change my circumstances of poverty by programming my brain with the kind of information that would guarantee academic success. That, I believed, would allow me to choose my own destiny.

I encountered negative people who tried to discourage me and put a lid on my dreams. I chose to regard them simply as environmental hazards to be carefully swept aside.

My strongest supporter and inspiration throughout this metamorphosis was my mother. She was one of 24 children, had only a third-grade education, and was married by age 13. She steadfastly encouraged my brother and me to read, though she never learned herself.

Many times, as I progressed from medical student to professor of neurological surgery, I was struck by the anatomical beauty of the brain and the extraordinary things medicine could do to improve the quality of life. Yet, at the same time, I became increasingly fascinated with the unbounded intellectual potential contained within that 1400-gram (3 pound) structure. The human brain, I came to realize, is simply a mechanical component of an entity of far greater beauty and power: the mind. I was awed by what an inspired and disciplined mind could accomplish.

Within every child's brain is a mind teeming with ideas and dreams and abilities unrealized. The greatest thing we can do—as parents, teachers, and friends—is to nourish that potential, both intellectual and humanitarian, so that each mind can fulfill its promise to the benefit of humankind.

"Within every child's brain is a mind teeming with ideas and dreams and abilities unrealized."

GLOSSARY

Angle of incidence—The angle at which light enters a new medium.

Angle of refraction—The amount of refraction determined by the index of refraction of the medium and the angle of incidence at which light hits it.

Anterior—The front of a living creature or structure; toward the front.

Aqueous humor— A clear fluid between the lens and the cornea of the eye.

Astigmatism—An irregularity in the surface of the cornea that prevents light from focusing accurately and results in a blurred image.

Axon—A thin and usually long extension of a nerve cell; carries impulses away from the cell body.

Binocular vision—Use of both eyes for vision.

Brain stem—A small, cordlike structure in the center of the brain.

Camera obscura—A darkened space with a small hole in one wall, which acts as a lens to project an image.

CAT—Computerized axial tomography, a type of scan used to study the structure of brain tissue.

Cell body—The operational center of the neuron; contains the nucleus of the cell.

Cerebellum—The small, densely striped structure that lies below and to the back of the brain; processes balance and coordination.

Cerebral cortex—The wrinkled gray covering of the cerebrum where millions of neurons make sense out of the signals that come into the brain.

Cerebrum—Anterior portion of the brain, consisting of two hemispheres; the most prominent part of the human brain.

Ciliary muscles—A ring of delicate fibers that hold the lens of the eye in place.

Cone—A type of photoreceptor that distinguishes color and detects fine details in objects.

Cornea—The curved, transparent, outer surface of the eyeball; covers the iris and pupil and lets light through to the inside of the eye.

Dendrite—Branch that extends from the cell body and receives incoming information.

Depth perception—The ability to convert a flattened image from the retina into a three-dimensional image.

Dorsal—The top of a living creature or structure; near the back.

EEG—Electroencephalography, a type of scan used to study the activity levels in the brain; also electroencephalograph, a medical instrument that records electric currents generated by the brain.

Field of vision—The entire space visible at a given instant without moving the eyes.

GLOSSARY

Focal Length—The distance from the lens to the point where the refracted light rays converge at the focal point.

Focus—The point at which all rays of light refract or bend together.

Fovea—A small depression in the center of the macula.

Frontal lobe—The front of the cerebrum; processes thought, reason, and emotion.

Glial cells—Cells in the nervous system, particularly the brain and spinal cord, that support and nourish the neurons.

Hemisphere—Either half of the brain.

Hyperopia—Farsightedness, an abnormal condition in which vision for distant objects is better than for near objects.

Image—The object formed when light rays come together to focus.

Image focus distance—The distance between the lens and the screen on which a projected image is focused.

Inferior—A structure that lies below another.

Iris—The colored part around the pupil of the eye; made of a series of circular muscles that constrict to make the pupil smaller in bright light or larger in dim light.

Lacrimal gland—The part of the eye where tears are produced.

Learning—The acquisition of new knowledge and skills.

Lens—A clear, curved object that has a different index of refraction than its surrounding medium; a clear part of the eye that focuses rays of light so as to form an image on the retina.

Lobe—A region of the cerebrum.

Macula—A spot on the retina that contains most of the eye's cone cells and few blood vessels.

Memory—The process of retrieving knowledge and bits of information related to skills that are stored in the brain; the store of things learned and kept in the mind.

Mnemonic device—A strategy, such as a phrase or formula, that increases the effectiveness of memory.

Motor neurons—The cells that send information to the muscles.

MRI—Magnetic resonance imaging, a type of scan used to study the structure of brain tissue.

Myopia—Nearsightedness, a vision abnormality in which distant objects appear blurred.

Neuron—A communication cell found in the brain and nervous system.

Neurotransmitter—A chemical, such as dopamine and adrenaline, that is released when an electric impulse reaches the end of an axon.

GLOSSARY

Occipital lobe—The back of the cerebrum; processes visual information.

Optic chiasm—The point where the optic nerves from both eyes join.

Optic disk—The point where the optic nerve enters the retina and which is not sensitive to light; also known as the blind spot.

Optic nerve—A thick bundle formed by the millions of neurons carrying information from the photoreceptors in the retina.

Parietal lobe—The upper side of the cerebrum; processes movement.

Peripheral vision—The vision at the sides, top, and bottom of a person's visual field.

PET—Positron emission tomography, a type of scan used to study the activity levels in the brain.

Posterior—The back of a living creature or structure; the hind end of the body.

Projected image—An inverted, reversed image formed on a surface by light passing through a convex lens.

Pupil—The dark circular opening in the center of the iris; contracts and expands to regulate the amount of light entering the eye.

Refraction—The bending of light at the point of contact between two different media.

Retina—A thin, translucent layer lining the back of the eye; receives images formed by the lens; connected to the brain by the optic nerve.

Rod—A type of photoreceptor shaped like a rod that responds to dim light.

Sclera—The tough white or bluish white covering that surrounds the eyeball and helps it maintain its shape.

Sensory neuron—A nerve cell that sends information from sense organs to the brain.

Superior—A structure that lies above another.

Synapse—A tiny gap that separates the axon of one neuron and the dendrite of another neuron; the point at which a nerve impulse passes from one neuron to another.

Tapetum—A shiny layer that lines the area behind the retina of many animals; helps make the eye visible in the dark and allows the animal to see better at night.

Temporal lobe—The bottom of the cerebrum; processes speech and language.

Ventral—The bottom of a living creature or structure; near the belly.

Visual cortex—The back of the brain; processes information from both eyes to form a complete image.

Vitreous humor—The clear, colorless jelly that fills the eyeball behind the lens and holds the internal structures of the eye in place while maintaining the shape of the eye.